RULES AND METHODS FOR CALCULATING THE PHYSICO-CHEMICAL PROPERTIES OF PARAFFINIC HYDROCARBONS

RULES AND METHODS FOR CALCULATING THE PHYSICO-CHEMICAL PROPERTIES OF PARAFFINIC HYDROCARBONS

by

V. M. TATEVSKII, V. A. BENDERSKII

and

S. S. YAROVOI

Translated from the Russian by
MARGARET F. MULLINS

Translation edited by
B. P. MULLINS
Senior Principal Scientific Officer,
Ministry of Aviation, Farnborough, Hampshire

PERGAMON PRESS

NEW YORK · OXFORD · LONDON · PARIS

1961

PERGAMON PRESS INC.
122 East 55th Street, New York 22, N.Y.
Statler Center 640, 900 Wilshire Boulevard,
Los Angeles 17, California

PERGAMON PRESS LTD.
Headington Hill Hall, Oxford
4 & 5 Fitzroy Square, London W.1

PERGAMON PRESS S.A.R.L.
24 Rue des Écoles, Paris Vᵉ

PERGAMON PRESS G.m.b.H.
Kaiserstrasse 75, Frankfurt am Main

A translation of the original volume

' *Zakonomernosti i metody rascheta*
fiziko-khimicheskikh svoistv
parafinovykh uglevodorodov '

Moscow, Gostoptekhizdat, 1960

Library of Congress Card No. 61-11533

Printed in Great Britain by
PERGAMON PRINTING & ART SERVICES LTD.,
LONDON

CONTENTS

CALCULATION OF PROPERTIES OF PARAFFIN HYDROCARBONS

vi

CONTENTS

Set by Vi Leach

TRANSLATION EDITOR'S FOREWORD

This is a unique monograph on a subject which has been pioneered by the authors and their co-workers. The first two methods of calculation, whereby the partial contributions of individual types of chemical bonds to a given physico-chemical property - deduced from known physico-chemical data on the lower alkanes (methane to octanes) - are summed appropriately over the whole molecule for any unknown higher alkane (nonanes, decanes or undecanes), are mathematically neat and described fully with many numerical examples. The third method involves the comparison of two physico-chemical properties of alkanes of the same or of different 'homologous groups' and has its range of uses too. The publication of these methods of calculation in the English language in book form makes accessible to a wide readership a branch of research hitherto little publicized. It is to be hoped that this monograph will prove not only to be directly useful to research scientists interested in paraffinic hydrocarbons, but that it may also stimulate others to develop these calculation techniques to embrace many other classes of organic molecules, non-hydrocarbons as well as hydrocarbons.

B.P.M.

Farnborough, Hants.
March, 1961

PREFACE

The purpose of this book is to give a presentation of the best methods developed during the last 10 years for calculating the physico-chemical properties of paraffinic hydrocarbons (alkanes) and especially of the higher ones.

The methods of calculation are presented in such a way that it is possible for them to be used readily by either the research chemist or the engineer, the graduate or the student working in the field of synthesis or research on the physico-chemical properties of hydrocarbons, and the designer or the technologist working in the chemical industry or the petroleum processing industry.

In the book all the necessary initial data are given for the calculation of molecular volumes, densities, heats of combustion, heats of formation from elements, latent heats of vaporization, vapour pressures, boiling points and some other properties of the higher paraffinic hydrocarbons.

Calculations of many properties of the $C_5 - C_{10}$ alkanes and certain properties of the C_{11} alkanes, for which there are no experimental data, have been accomplished by the authors; the results are given in a completed form.

By using this book and the monograph [31], it is possible to extend the methods of calculation given here primarily for alkanes, to other hydrocarbons (alkenes, alkynes, alkadienes, cycloalkanes, alkylbenzenes, etc.) and also to organic compounds of other classes.

In the completion of some calculations, the results of which appear later, students of the Moscow State University took part - N. Nikitin (Tables 2, 3, 13 and 14), V.A. Ziborov (Table 13) and A.A. Boldin (Tables 9, 10) - to whom the authors extend their thanks.

INTRODUCTION

Paraffinic hydrocarbons (alkanes) form a very important part of petroleum and of diverse petroleum products. A knowledge of the physico-chemical properties of hydrocarbons is necessary for the resolution of many scientific and technical problems, in particular for the determination of the fractional composition of petroleum and motor fuels, the isolation of individual hydrocarbons or data on the composition of mixtures of hydrocarbons from fractions of petroleum and synthetic fuels, etc.

The very important physico-chemical properties of hydrocarbons in general and alkanes in particular, a knowledge of which is necessary for the solution of the problems referred to above, are as follows: heat of formation and the change in free energy during formation from elements, specific heat, heat of combustion, density or molecular volume, boiling point, vapour pressure, temperature of crystallization, latent heats of vaporization and crystallization, viscosity, surface tension, refraction and some others.

The experimental determination of all these properties, even for hydrocarbons with a small number of carbon atoms, is very difficult because of the difficulties in obtaining individual hydrocarbons of high purity and of the difficulty in the precise measurement of their physico-chemical properties. At the present time more or less complete and reliable data on the standard physico-chemical properties are obtainable only for alkanes with a number of carbon atoms $n \leqslant 8$, that is, no higher than octanes. For nonanes there exists fragmentary and incomplete data, and for decanes and higher hydrocarbons there are virtually no data. It should be noted that nowadays we cannot hope for a speedy determination of experimental data on the physico-chemical properties of the higher alkanes ($C_{10} - C_{20}$), since this task is of great magnitude and impossible to complete with the effort available in the next few years.

Amongst the $C_{11} - C_{12}$ hydrocarbons and higher ones there are

1

a large number of isomers which are not synthetically obtainable at present, and not only the determination of their physico-chemical properties, but also the development of methods of synthesizing them in a number of instances present a serious problem. On the other hand the higher C_{11} — C_{20} hydrocarbons present the greatest interest at the moment since they are components of the ligroin and kerosine fractions of petroleum and corresponding products of interest nowadays to the petroleum and chemical industries.

A knowledge of the physico-chemical constants of the higher alkanes (included are those that have not been synthesized nor studied experimentally) is necessary for the solution of many problems.

One of these problems is the verification of the accuracy of the structure, ascribed again to the synthesized higher alkanes. Actually in the synthesis of the new higher alkanes, it is still far from possible, in the course of the synthetic reactions, to reach a well-defined and indisputable conclusion as to the structure of a newly synthesized alkane. One of the methods of verifying the accuracy of the structural formula ascribed to a new alkane is the experimental determination of its basic physico-chemical constants (density or molecular volume, refractions, vapour pressure, boiling point, heat of combustion, latent heat of vaporization, etc.) and a comparison of the experimental results with those calculated theoretically, for example by the methods described below.

The second problem, for the solution of which it is necessary to calculate the physico-chemical properties of the higher alkanes, is to establish the isomeric composition, even if approximate, of the saturated fractions of petroleum or of synthetic hydrocarbon fuel. Actually, for an estimate of the possible isomeric composition of narrow fractions during straight-run distillation of the saturated fractions of petroleum or saturated fractions of a synthetic motor fuel containing only alkanes it is necessary to know at least the basic physico-chemical constants of the separate isomers or of the higher alkanes having properties nearest to the group of isomers in question. First of all, it is necessary to know the boiling point and vapour pressure of the isomeric alkanes. Moreoever, in the evaluation of the possible isomeric composition of narrow fractions of petroleum or synthetic fuel, it is extremely useful to have a knowledge of such physico-chemical properties of the higher isomeric alkanes as density (or molecular volume), refraction, latent heat of vaporization, heat of combustion, etc.

A knowledge of these constants of the isomeric higher alkanes permits the making of an approximate estimate of the
isomeric composition of the technical and synthetic fractions,
containing higher alkanes.

Furthermore, in the distillation of fractions of petroleum
or synthetic fuel it is possible to determine the feasibility
of separating by distillation the individual supposed isomers,
the components of the fraction, and to determine the optimum
conditions for distillation only if values of the vapour pressure of the isomeric alkanes for a certain temperature inter-
val are available.

For the majority of isomers of the higher alkanes at the
present time these values can only be established by means
of calculation, for example by one of the methods described
above.

Finally, individual hydrocarbons or their mixtures, used in
practice as fuel, should possess somewhat well-defined values
of some physico-chemical properties. These properties include
density, heat of combustion, crystallization temperature,
boiling point, viscosity and certain others.

The question is, if hydrocarbons of a given class (for
example, individual alkanes) exist possessing the specified
group of physico-chemical properties, is it possible to solve
this problem by calculating the properties of all the separate isomers of the hydrocarbons of a given class (for example
alkanes), in particular using the methods set out below.

Thus a series of technically important problems, briefly
indicated above, requires a knowledge of the physico-chemical
constants of the individual isomers of the higher alkanes.
As has already been mentioned, the values of the physico-
chemical constants for the majority of the individual isomers
of the higher alkanes are not obtainable yet experimentally
and can be found only by means of calculations; the best
developed methods of calculation, at the present time, are
described below.

Methods of calculation of physico-chemical properties of
alkanes began to be worked out long ago. However, because
there were an insufficient number of and insufficiently
accurate data on isomers of branched structure, the primary

attention of the investigations was focussed on alkanes, mainly of normal structure; for n-alkanes, simple rules were established for certain properties possessing the character of capacity coefficients - refraction, heat of formation from elements, heat of combustion and certain other coefficients. The essence of these rules consisted of the fact that for alkanes of normal structure, their physico-chemical characteristics, enumerated above, are linear functions of the number of carbon atoms to a very good approximation.

These rules were interpreted in such a way that for the C atom in different n-alkanes there have to be constant values of the partial refraction, heat of formation, heat of combustion, etc. Another way of interpreting these rules arose from the fact that to the C—C and C—H bonds are attributed constant partial values of the specified quantities, independently of which n-alkane contains these bonds. However, these notions serve to explain only those rules (linear variation with n) which hold for certain properties of n-alkanes. The experimental determination of the properties of the isomeric alkanes showed that various isomers with an equal number of carbon atoms differ significantly in their properties from the n-alkanes.

It is natural that these differences arouse considerable practical interest, because on them is based the sub-division of the isomeric alkanes and the determination of the separate isomers or groups of isomers in mixtures of alkanes, among them the corresponding fractions of petroleum and motor fuel.

Since the experimental determination of all the physico-chemical properties of isomers of alkanes of practical interest would be a huge task, demanding large expenditure in capital and time, naturally a great interest is taken in the development of theoretical, semi-empirical or even purely empirical methods of calculating the physico-chemical properties of alkanes and especially of the higher alkanes. However, up to the last ten years, research devoted to this cause was either concerned mainly with n-alkanes, or possessed a purely empirical character and related only to certain groups of alkanes, or did not provide sufficient accuracy. In the research by Rossini and his co-workers [1, 2], for example, linear variations were established between the heat of combustion of the n-alkanes and the number of carbon atoms. Furthermore, the linear variations were made a little more accurate [3] by the introduction of a small quadratic term relating to n.

Later Ewell [4] put forward the supposition that the heats
of combustion of alkanes of branched structure are subject
to an empirical law, based on the fact that each simple
branching of the chain (tertiary C atom) changes its heat of
combustion, as compared to a chain of normal structure, by
1.8 cals/mol and each complex branching (quaternary C atom)
by 4.7 cals/mol, independently of the number and relative
distribution in the molecule of these branchings. This rule,
apart from the fact that it was purely empirical, finally
proved to be inaccurate. Later Ewell found an approximate
empirical rule, concerning the variation of the entropy of
the alkane with the number of simple (tertiary C atom) and
complex (quaternary C atom) branchings.

Other investigators studied the question of the variation
of latent heats of vaporization, vapour pressures and other
properties of the alkanes with respect to their structures
and gave a series of empirical equations [5-9]. Tilicheyev
and Iogansen [10, 11] found the equations which represented
very accurately the variation of the boiling points of n-
alkanes and 2-methylalkanes with the number of carbon atoms
in the molecule: Tilicheyev and Tatevskii [12] found the
equations for the critical pressures of the n-alkanes.

Kireyev [13, 14] and then Karapet'yants [15, 16] in the calculation of certain properties of hydrocarbons used a comparative method of calculation, based on the fact that one
property in a series of compounds is determined by another
property. Another variant of the comparative method of calculation was based on the determination of a given property
of a series of compounds from an analogous property of another series of compounds (for more details see [15, 16]).

With the help of these methods values were obtained of
various physico-chemical properties of certain alkanes, e.g.
of the critical pressures. However, in all the researches
referred to above, the rules obtained had an empirical
character. A system had not been developed based on the idea
of factors determining the physico-chemical properties of
alkanes, which would at once permit the devising of rules
covering a wide range of physico-chemical properties of alkanes and which would embrace all the fields of their isomers. Such an attempt was made by one of the authors and
co-workers in a series of reports, published in about 1950
[19-46]. Later Bernstein [17] set up a scheme for the calculation of the energy of formation of hydrocarbons based on
other ideas, and obtained interesting results; however,

B

Bernstein's method, because of its extreme unwieldiness in
the general case, was not used by its author for concrete
calculations. Besides that, as shown in [46], this method
in its final results was essentially equivalent to the method
developed in the cited reports [19-46] which in practice is
far more convenient. In the work of Bagdasaryan [47] and
Laider [18] an attempt was made to devise a scheme for calculating certain physico-chemical properties of hydrocarbons
based on concepts that are a simplification of the ideas,
developed in the preceding reports [19-46] and described below. This attempt cannot be regarded as successful, since
the simplifications introduced into our scheme of calculation,
were not substantiated theoretically in these reports and were
not acceptable practically, since they magnified considerably
the errors in calculation.

A detailed survey of the fundamental methods of calculation
of the energies of formation (and to some extent, other
physico-chemical properties) of alkanes, a comparison and
analysis of the discrepancies between the different methods,
and also an analysis of the theoretical questions concerned,
are given in the report [46].

We will not dwell here on other reports devoted to methods
of calculation of the physico-chemical properties of alkanes,
since the majority of them possess a purely empirical character and do not solve the question of the creation of a single
scheme of calculation embracing a wide range of physico-
chemical properties of all the isomeric alkanes; some of
them were based on wrong theoretical ideas and do not introduce anything substantially new in comparison with the methods
described below and give less accuracy. A useful, though incomplete résumé of the literature is contained in the work of
Rossini and Greenshields to which the reader is referred.

All the methods described below for calculating the physico-
chemical properties of alkanes are based on theoretical ideas
developed by one of the authors in the cited series of reports
[19-46]. These theoretical ideas in a general way relate to
the different physico-chemical properties of all sorts of
classes of compounds. In this book, however, only those theoretical ideas are used which are necessary for the explanation
of the rules, considered below, of the physico-chemical properties of alkanes and the foundation of the methods of calculation of these properties.

The problems worked out in Chapter III (the comparative

method of calculation of the physico-chemical properties of
alkanes) were reported on the basis of the theoretical concepts developed in the above mentioned reports of one of the
authors; the results reported here are the direct consequen-
ces of these ideas; however, as has already been noted, the
comparative method of calculation by itself was already used
for the physico-chemical properties of different compounds a
relatively long time ago and was developed in the U.S.S.R. in
the reports of Kireyev [13,14], and especially in later years
in the reports of Karapet'yants [15,16]. The particular fea-
ture of the principles set out here of the comparative method
of calculation for alkanes is the fact that this method
arises automatically as a consequence of the concepts both
of the branched alkanes from homologous groups and of the
approximately linear laws established by us earlier for such
groups for a varying series of physico-chemical properties.
The establishment of the concept of homologous groups of
branched alkanes, appearing as a result of general theoretical information concerning the factors determining the properties of the chemical bonds, developed by one of the
authors, is in our opinion the most essential point in the
theory of the comparative method of calculation for alkanes.
Analogous results, as obtained from [35, 36] will be included
for many other classes of organic compounds, including other
classes of hydrocarbons.

The aim of this book is the application of the laws derived
by us for physico-chemical properties and the methods of calculation of the physico-chemical properties developed on the
basis of these laws, permitting the derivation of sufficiently
accurate and reliable values of these magnitudes for mass
calculation of the physico-chemical properties of alkanes.
In this book the results are generalized with regard to alkanes and the numerical constants obtained in the preceding
reports [19-46] are made more specific by using new data;
also the range of physico-chemical properties and the range
of hydrocarbons to which the numerical methods apply are both
enlarged. It will be seen below that the methods described
here are completely suitable for the calculation of the
physico-chemical quantities of hundreds of higher alkanes.

CHAPTER I

THEORETICAL IDEAS AND EXPERIMENTAL DATA.
FIRST METHOD OF CALCULATION

1. Basic Ideas and Equations

It is known that many physico-chemical properties of normal alkanes obey simple laws. Such properties as the molar
heat of formation or refraction can be considered as the sums
of the appropriate quantities due to the separate chemical
bonds in normal alkanes. For example, the refraction relative to one molecule $\frac{R_M}{N_A}$ (where R_M is the molecular refraction, N_A is Avagadro's number) can be expressed for the normal alkane C_nH_{2n+2} as the sum of the refractions r_{C-C} and
r_{C-H} of the separate C—C and C—H bonds in the normal
alkane:

$$\frac{R_M}{V_A} = (n-1)\,r_{C-C} + (2n+2)\,r_{C-H} \, .$$

Multiplying this equation by N_A and substituting the sym-
bols $R_{C-C} = N_A\,r_{C-C}$ and $R_{C-H} = N_A\,r_{C-H}$ for the refractions N_A
of the C—C and C—H bonds we obtain the very well-known
formula*

$$R_M = (n-1)\,R_{C-C} + (2n+2)\,R_{C-H} \, . \tag{1}$$

Analogous formulae were established for other physico-

---

*Henceforth we will call the quantities R_{C-C} (or R_{C-H}) and analogous quantities
for other physico-chemical properties, relating to N_A and the bonds C—C (or
C—H) the quantities due to the corresponding bond, as is usually done.

chemical properties of normal alkanes*. Equation (1) for
and similar equations have often been used and are being used
up to the present (especially in chemical synthesis) for the
calculation of the physico-chemical properties not only of
normal but also of branched alkanes. In many synthetic
studies for the verification of the purity of synthesized
branched alkanes, the values of refraction (or other magnitudes) measured experimentally are equal to those calculated
according to the reduced formula for R_M .

Such an extension of the formulae (1) and (1a) for refraction and for other analogous quantities to branched paraffins
is completely incorrect. The physico-chemical properties of
branched alkanes, as a rule, differ from the properties of
the normal alkanes and these differences (see below) are
often quite significant. A comparison of the experimental
values of the physico-chemical parameters of branched alkanes
with those calculated according to formulae similar to (1),
cannot therefore either verify the structure or give a crite-
rion of the branched paraffin.

Formulae (1) and (1a) are not suitable for branched paraffins. In the reports [19-46] it is shown that for a reflec-
tion of the experimental laws of some physico-chemical properties, not only of normal but also of any branched alkanes,
it is necessary to suppose that the properties of the C—C
bonds (likewise for the C—H bonds) in alkanes are different
and depend on the influences to which these bonds are subjec-
ted by the atoms surrounding them and primarily the influences
of the nearest atoms surrounding the C—C (or C—H) bond,
i.e. the bonds directly attached to one of the atoms.

If the study of the effect on a given C—C (or C—H) bond
is restricted to the nearest ring of atoms referred to above,
then, as was mentioned earlier, we ought to consider four
forms (or sub-types) in all of the C—H bond and ten forms
(or sub-types) of the C—C bond (Table 1). Since the C_0—H
and C_1—C_1 bonds are encountered only in methane and ethane,

---

*Sometimes in place of formula (1) the formula is used:

$$R_M = nR_C + (2n + 2) R_H,$$
(1a)

where R_C and R_H are refractions for one gramme-atom of C and H , respectively.

This formula as can be seen is equivalent to formula (1) and also is only
correct for normal alkanes.

respectively, in the remaining paraffinic hydrocarbons, beginning with propane, it is possible to encounter only three
types of C_i—H bond $(i = 1, 2, 3)$ and nine types of C_i—C_j
bond $(i, j = 1, 2, 3, 4;\ i \leqslant j)$.

Most important was the supposition that for the C_i—C_j (or
C_i—H) bond of each type there is only one value of the
physico-chemical quantity under consideration, independently
of the alkane molecule in which this bond is situated.   In
agreement with this supposition, any physico-chemical quantity
(we will denote it by P), e.g. molecular refraction, for the
alkane C_nH_{2n+2} (normal or branched) per mole of hydrocarbon
can be written in the form

$$P = \sum_{i=0}^{3} n_i p_i + \sum_{i \leqslant j = 1}^{4} n_{ij} p_{ij}. \qquad (2)$$

where n_i = no. of C—H bonds of the type C—H in a molecule
        of the alkane in question;

   p_i = value of the quantity P, corresponding to the N_A
        bonds of type C_i—H ;

   n_{ij} = no. of C—C bonds of the type C_i—C_i in a mole-
        cule of alkane;

   p_{ij} = value of the quantity P, corresponding to the N_A
        bonds of type C_i—C_j .

Evidently, the numbers n_i and n_{ij} are directly calculable
from the structural formula and even from the carbon skeleton
of the alkane. The determination of the numbers n_i and n_{ij}
from the carbon skeleton of the alkane will be explained for
the example 2,2-dimethyl-3-ethylheptane, for which the carbon skeleton has the formula

$$
\begin{array}{c}
C_1 \\
| \\
C_1 - C_4 - C_3 - C_2 - C_2 - C_2 - C_1 \\
\,\,| \quad\;\; | \\
C_1 \;\; C_2 \\
\quad\;\; | \\
\quad\;\; C_1
\end{array}
$$

Here the suffices 1, 2, 3, 4 indicate primary, secondary,
tertiary and quaternary atoms, respectively. As can be seen
from the reduced formula, the numbers n_i and n_{ij} of the
C_i—H and C_i—C_j bonds of the different forms (sub-types)

will be

$$n_1 = 15, \quad n_2 = 8, \quad n_3 = 1, \quad n_{12} = 2, \quad n_{13} = 0, \quad n_{14} = 3, \quad n_{22} = 2,$$
$$n_{23} = 2, \quad n_{24} = 0, \quad n_{33} = 0, \quad n_{34} = 1, \quad n_{44} = 0.$$

Consequently, for the given hydrocarbon, equation (2) will possess the following form:

$$P = 15p_1 + 8p_2 + p_3 + 2p_{12} + 3p_{14} + 2p_{22} + 2p_{23} + p_{34}.$$

Equation (2) contains 12 quantities p_i and p_{ij} , which as yet we have not determined. In principle these quantities, that is the partial values of the magnitude P , corresponding to the C_i-C_j or C_i-H bonds of a given type could be calculated by substituting experimental values of the quantity $\overset{\prime}{P}$ on the left-hand side for a series of alkanes (not less than 12) and solving the system of equations obtained with respect to the p_i and p_{ij} . However, the equations obtained by this means are linearly dependent, and from them 12 quantities p_i and p_{ij} could not be determined, since the coefficients n_i and n_{ij} are connected together by the three equations (3):

$$n_1 = 3n_{12} + 3n_{13} + 3n_{14},$$
$$n_2 = 2n_{22} + n_{12} + n_{23} + n_{24},$$
$$n_3 = \frac{2}{3} n_{33} + \frac{1}{3} n_{13} \frac{1}{3} n_{23} + \frac{1}{3} n_{34}. \tag{3}$$

Substituting these expressions for n_1, n_2 and n_3 in (2) we obtain

$$P = \sum_{i \leqslant j = 1}^{4} n_{ij}P_{ij} = n_{12}P_{12} + n_{13}P_{13} + n_{14}P_{14} + n_{22}P_{22} + n_{23}P_{23} +$$
$$+ n_{24}P_{24} - n_{33}P_{33} + n_{34}P_{34} + n_{44}P_{44}, \tag{4}$$

where the quantities P_{ij} are expressed in terms of p_i and p_{ij} according to the formulae:

$$P_{12} = p_{12} + 3p_1 + p_2, \qquad P_{23} = p_{23} + p_2 + \frac{1}{3} p_3,$$

$$P_{13} = p_{13} + 3p_1 + \frac{1}{3} p_3, \qquad P_{24} = p_{24} + p_2,$$

$$P_{14} = p_{14} + 3p_1, \qquad\qquad P_{33} = p_{33} + \frac{2}{3} p_3, \tag{5}$$

$$P_{22} = p_{22} + 2p_2, \qquad\qquad P_{34} = p_{34} + \frac{1}{3}\,p_3,$$
$$P_{44} = p_{44}.$$

$$(5)$$

Or, in a general form

$$P_{ij} = p_{ij} + \left(\frac{4-i}{i}\right) p_i + \left(\frac{4-j}{j}\right) p_j.$$

The physical concept of the quantity P_{ij} lies in the fact that these quantities present specific combinations of the quantities p_i and p_{ij} , relating to the specific C_i—C_j , C_i—H bonds in a molecule of alkane, that is the numbers P_{ij} are values of physico-chemical quantities relating not to the one C_i—C_j or C_i—H bond but to a specific combination of these bonds.

Substituting experimentally determined values of the quantities P in the left-hand side of equation (4) for a series of alkanes (not less than for nine alkanes), we obtain a system of equations for the as yet unknown nine magnitudes P_{ij} . Having obtained the latter from experimental data for the investigated alkanes, we can then use them for the calculation of the magnitudes P for the non-investigated ones, including the higher alkanes.

It is natural that the values of the properties P derived in this manner for the experimentally non-investigated alkanes, including the higher ones, can be considered reliable only in those cases when the equation (4) describes accurately the law for the change in the properties P for all the alkanes investigated, i.e. if all the known experimental data for the property P for alkanes is reflected accurately by equation (4) for any specific numerical values P_{ij} , obtained from available experimental results, e.g. by the method of least squares.

This raises two very important questions:

i) what physico-chemical quantities for alkanes can be described by equation (4)?

ii) with what accuracy does equation (4) describe the experimental laws for the variation of these magnitudes from alkane to alkane?

A study of the experimental data shows that equations (2) or (4) more or less reflect the laws for the following properties of alkanes: molecular volume V, molecular refraction R, heats of formation of alkanes from their elements ΔH (el.), heats of formation of alkanes from the free atoms ΔH (at.), heats of combustion ΔH (comb.), latent heats of vaporization L (vap.), logarithms of the vapour pressure log p, magnetic susceptibility $\varkappa$ and, somewhat less accurately, the free energy (thermodynamic potential) of formation from the elements ΔZ [19-46].

2. Molecular Volumes

Equation (4) for molecular volumes takes the form

$$V_M = \sum_{i<j=1}^{4} n_{ij}V_{ij}. \qquad (4a)$$

The values V_{ij}, calculated by us for 20° and 25°C, are given in Table 2. A comparison of the experimental and calculated values for V_M^{20} is given in Table 13 and Fig. 1. The agreement is completely satisfactory except for the individual cases where the error exceeds 1 ml./mole. Formula (4a) gives basically the isomeric effect and the experimental laws for the change of the molecular volumes of alkanes.

3. Molecular Refractions

For molecular refraction, equation (4) would take the form

$$R_M = \sum_{i<j=1}^{4} n_{ij}R_{ij}. \qquad (4b)$$

The values for R_{ij} calculated by us are given in Table 3 for 20° and 25°.

A comparison of the experimental and calculated values R_M^{20} and R_M^{25} is shown in Table 14 and Fig. 2. For comparison, in the vast majority of cases (with a few exceptions), use was made only of those alkanes for which both the constants n_D^{20} and d_4^{20} (n_D^{25} and d_4^{25}) were determined completely reliably to known and very accurate standards.

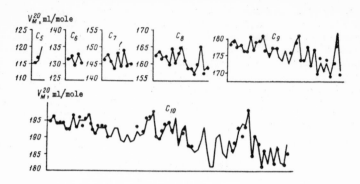

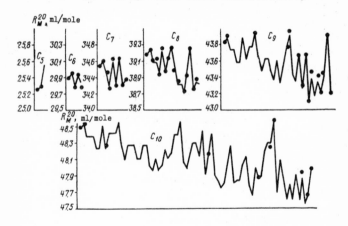

Fig. 1

Values of V_{M}^{20} for the alkanes C_5-C_{10}, experimental
(points) and calculated according to equation (4a)
(lines)

The points, corresponding to the isomeric alkanes, are given for
a series of investigations on isomeric alkanes in Table 13

Fig. 2

Values of R_{M}^{20} for the alkanes C_5-C_{10}, experimental
(points) and calculated according to equation (4b)
(lines)

The points, corresponding to the isomeric alkanes, are given for
a series of investigations on isomeric alkanes in Table 14

As is evident from Table 14 the error in calculation amounts
as a rule, to 0.01-0.03 ml/mole and nowhere exceeds 0.07 ml./
mole; although the differences in the refractions of some
isomeric alkanes amounts to 0.80 ml./mole. In this way, the
calculation gives the isomeric effect completely satisfactorily.

4. Latent Heats of Vaporization

Equation (4) is used also for latent heats of vaporization
of alkanes in an ideal gaseous state. Denoting by $L°$ the
latent heat of vaporization for one mole in an ideal gaseous
state, we can write equation (4) in the form

$$L° = \sum_{i \leqslant j = 1}^{4} n_{ij} L_{ij}. \tag{4c}$$

For the calculation it is more convenient to write this
equation in the form

$$\lambda° = \sum_{i \leqslant j = 1}^{4} n_{ij} \lambda_{ij}, \tag{4d}$$

where

$$\lambda = \frac{L°}{4.575}, \quad \lambda_{ij} = \frac{L_{ij}}{4.575}.$$

The values of L_{ij}, calculated by us for different temperature ranges, are given in Table 4. Tables 15 and 16 and Fig.
3 show a comparison of the values of $\lambda°$ and $L°$, calculated
according to equations (4c) and (4d) and according to the
experimental values of the vapour pressures of alkanes*. The
agreement can be considered satisfactory. Equations (4c) and
(4d) give basically the isomeric effect.

Subsequently, it will be more convenient to use the quantity
$\lambda°$, the equation for which, (4d), is given above.

---

*The calculation of $L°$ from the experimental values of the vapour pressures of
alkanes ($L°$ exp.) was achieved from equation (6), and the values of $\lambda°$ from equation
(7). The vapour pressures of alkanes given in [51] were used.

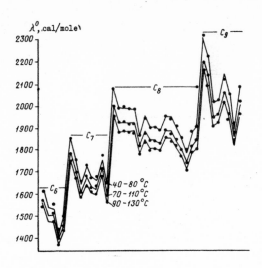

Fig. 3

Values of the quantities $\lambda^\circ = \dfrac{L^\circ_{\text{vap.}}}{4.575}$ for the alkanes C_6—C_9, experimental (points) and calculated according to equation (4d) (lines)

The points corresponding to the isomeric alkanes C_6–C_9 are given for a series of investigations on isomeric alkanes in Table 15. For the alkanes C_9 experiment and calculation are compared for eight alkanes, for which there are vapour pressure data

The values for λ_{ij} are presented in Table 5. The equations derived from the data in Table 5 for the dependency of λ_{ij} on absolute temperature T are expressed as

$$\lambda_{12} = 471 = \text{const},$$

$$\lambda_{13} = 392.39 - 0.0956 \ T,$$

$$\lambda_{14} = 314.45 - 0.0664 \ T,$$

$$\lambda_{22} = 391.08 - 0.4844 \ T,$$

$$\lambda_{23} = 273.92 - 0.4815 \ T,$$

$$\lambda_{24} = 234.64 - 0.5184 \ T,$$

$$\lambda_{33} = 285.21 - 0.6992 \ T,$$

$$\lambda_{34} = 252.61 - 0.7028 \ T.$$

5. Vapour Pressures

As is shown by an analysis of the experimental data, the constant B in the equation

$$\ln p = -\frac{L^\circ}{RT} + B \qquad (6)$$

and the constant b in the analogous equation

$$\ln p = -\frac{\lambda^\circ}{T} + b, \qquad (7)$$

where $\lambda^\circ = \frac{L(\text{vap.})}{4.575}$, $b = \frac{B}{2,30}$, can also be calculated for each temperature range according to formula (4):

$$B = \sum_{i \leqslant j = 1}^{4} n_{ij} b_{ij},$$

$$\qquad (4e)$$

$$b = \sum_{i \leqslant j = 1}^{4} n_{ij} b_{ij}.$$

Values of B_{ij} and b_{ij}, calculated by us for certain temperature ranges, are given in Tables 4 and 6. In Table 17 and on Fig. 4 there is a comparison of the values of b calculated according to equation $(4e)$ and from experimental data on the vapour pressure of hydrocarbons. The agreement can be considered satisfactory. The equations, derived from the data in Table 6, of the variation of the quantities B_{ij} with the absolute temperature T are:

$$b_{12} = 3.405 = \text{const},$$

$$b_{13} = 2.418 - 0.000294\ T,$$

$$b_{14} = 1.819 - 0.000204\ T,$$

$$b_{22} = 0.650 - 0.00118\ T,$$

or

$$b_{22} = -0.237 + 166.04\ T^{-1},$$

$$b_{23} = -0.440 - 0.00122\ T,$$

$$b_{24} = -0.972 - 0.00131\ T,$$

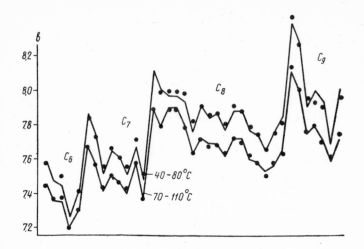

Fig. 4

Values of the constant b for the alkanes $C_6 - C_9$,
experimental, that is, calculated from the vapour
pressure (points) and calculated according to
equation (4e) (lines)

Series of investigations on alkanes, as in Fig.3

Starting from equation (4d) for λ° and equation (4e) for b,
it is easily seen that log p for a given T can be calculated according to the formula

$$\log p = \sum_{i \leqslant j=1}^{4} n_{ij}\pi_{ij}, \qquad (4f)$$

where

$$\pi_{ij} = -\frac{\lambda_{ij}}{T} + b_{ij}. \qquad (9)$$

Hence the values of the vapour pressure of the alkanes at
temperature T can also be expressed by the formula

$$p = 10^{\sum\limits_{i<j=1}^{4} n_{ij}\pi_{ij}} = \Pi\left(\Pi_{ij}^{n_{ij}}\right), \qquad (10)$$

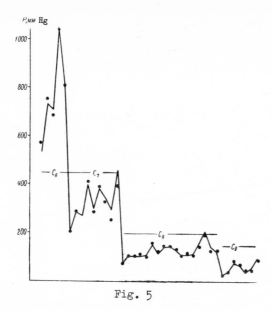

Fig. 5

Values of vapour pressure for the alkanes $C_6 - C_9$,
at a temperature of 60°C, experimental data from
[51] (points) and calculated according to [10]
(lines)

Series of investigations on alkanes, as in Fig.3

where

$$\Pi_{ij} = 10^{\pi_{ij}} . \qquad (11)$$

The values of the quantities π_{ij} and Π_{ij} for certain temperatures are given in Tables 7 and 8. A comparison of the
vapour pressures for some alkanes, both experimental and
calculated according to equation (10), is given in Fig. 5.
As can be seen from Fig. 5, the isomeric effect shows up
well from the calculation.

6. Heats of Formation from Free Atoms, Heats of Formation from Elements, Heat of Combustion and Free Energies of Formation from Elements

For these quantities, equation (4) is written in the following way:

$$\Delta H^\circ(\text{at.}) = \sum_{i \leqslant j = 1}^{4} n_{ij} H_{ij} \ (\text{at.}),$$

$$\Delta H^\circ(\text{el.}) = \sum_{i \leqslant j = 1}^{4} n_{ij} H_{ij} \ (\text{el.}),$$

$$\Delta H^\circ(\text{comb.}) = \sum_{i \leqslant j = 1}^{4} n_{ij} H_{ij} \ (\text{comb.}),$$

$$\Delta Z^\circ(\text{el.}) = \sum_{i \leqslant j = 1}^{4} n_{ij} Z_{ij} \ (\text{el.}).$$

(4g)

The last of these equations (for ΔZ° (el.) does not possess
the same accuracy as those preceding, since the distribution
of ΔZ (el.) per bond, as is done in (4g), cannot be strictly
substantiated.

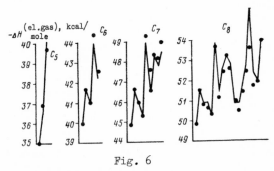

Fig. 6

Values of ΔH° (el.gas) for alkanes $C_5 - C_8$,
experimental according to data in [49,50]
(points) and calculated according to equation (4g) (lines)

Series of investigations on isomeric alkanes, as in Fig.2

Values of H_{ij} (at.), H_{ij} (el.), H_{ij} (comb.) and Z_{ij} (el.) for gaseous and liquid alkanes are given in Tables 9 and 10. A comparison of the experimental and calculated values of ΔH° (el. gas), ΔH° (comb.,liq.) is given in Table 18 and on Figs. 6 and 7 for the C_5—C_8 alkanes. The deviation of the calculated values from the experimental values of ΔZ (el.), and also ΔH° (at.), ΔH° (el.) and ΔH° (comb.) for 2,3-dimethylpentane cannot as yet be explained, since for the analogous hydrocarbon 2,3-dimethylhexane the agreement between the experimental and calculated values is satisfactory. The reason is assumed to be that the experimental values of ΔZ° (el.), ΔH° (at.), ΔH° (el.), ΔH° (comb.) for 2,3-dimethylpentane are not completely accurate*. The divergence between experiment and calculation for 2,2,4-trimethylpentane, 2,2,4,4-tetramethylpentane and 2,3,4,4-tetramethylpentane is explained, apparently, by the steric hindrances for normal rotation of the CH_3-group in these hydrocarbons, as this follows from the geometrical calculation**. In the remaining cases the agreement between the calculated and experimental values is satisfactory and calculation gives, to a large extent, the isomeric effect.

7. Reactions Between Alkanes of Arbitrary Structure

For a reversible reaction in which the reactants A, B etc. and the reaction products C, D, etc. are alkanes, we can get

$$\nu_A - A + \nu_B B + \ldots \rightleftarrows \nu_C C + \nu_D D. \tag{12}$$

The constant of equilibrium of such a reaction for substances under standard conditions is determined from the equation

$$RT \ln K_p = -\Delta Z^\circ = (\nu_A \Delta Z^\circ_A + \nu_B \Delta Z^\circ_B + \ldots) - \\ - (\nu_C \Delta Z^\circ_C + \nu_D \Delta Z^\circ_D + \ldots), \tag{13}$$

---

*Compare the analogous case of 2-methylproprane, for which the divergence between the experimental values and those calculated by us was eliminated after improving the experimental data of [3].
**Equation (4) was based on the supposition that all the valencies of carbon in alkanes are tetrahedrons, but the groups joined by ordinary bonds possess a "chess" arrangement [54]. This does not allow for energy effects that depend on steric hindrances and deflections from the chess arrangement of the groups which are possessed by some branched alkanes, for example, in alkanes with branchings in the positions 2,2 and 4 or 2,2 and 4,4 and similar ones. For the calculation of these energy effects in equation (4) it is necessary to introduce an addition constant-term δ for 2,2,4-trialkyl alkanes, 2 δ for 2,2,4,4-tetra-alkylalkanes etc. For example, the value of δ for the calculation of the heats of combustion of liquid alkanes at 298.16°K is equal to ~ 2.28 kcal/mol.

C

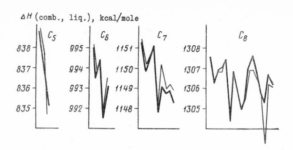

Fig. 7

Values of ΔH° (comb.,liq.) for $C_5 - C_8$, experimental according to data in [49] (thin lines) and calculated according to equation (4g) (thick lines)

Series of investigations on isomeric alkanes, as in Fig.2

where ΔZ_A° is the change in the thermodynamic potential during the formation of one mole of alkane A at standard conditions from elementary carbon (graphite) and molecular hydrogen. Similar meanings are possessed by the symbols ΔZ_B°, ΔZ_C°, ΔZ_D° etc.

From (13) we obtain

$$K_p = \frac{\left(e^{-\frac{\Delta Z_C^\circ}{RT}}\right)^{\nu C}\left(e^{-\frac{\Delta Z_D^\circ}{RT}}\right)^{\nu D}\cdots}{\left(e^{-\frac{\Delta Z_A^\circ}{RT}}\right)^{\nu A}\left(e^{-\frac{\Delta Z_B^\circ}{RT}}\right)^{\Delta B}\cdots} . \tag{14}$$

The multipliers occurring in equation (14) can be converted into the basis for equation (4) in the following way:

$$\left(e^{-\frac{\Delta Z_A^\circ}{RT}}\right)^{\nu A} = \left(e^{\frac{-\sum n_{ij}^{(A)} Z_{ij}(\text{el.})}{RT}}\right)^{\nu A} = \Pi_A\, (\zeta_{ij})^{n_{ij}^{(A)}\nu_A}, \tag{15}$$

where

$$\zeta_{ij} = e^{-\frac{Z_{ij}(\text{el.})}{RT}}, \tag{16}$$

and the product Π_A holds for all $C_i - C_j$ bonds of the different sub-types in a molecule of alkane A .

The other multipliers in equation (14) could be converted, similarly to (15). Then we would get instead of (14)

$$K_p = \frac{\Pi_C \, (\zeta_{ij})^{n_{ij}^C \, \nu_C} \, \Pi_D \, (\zeta_{ij})^{n_{ij}^D \, \nu_D}}{\Pi_A \, (\zeta_{ij})^{n_{ij}^A \, \nu_A} \, \Pi_B \, (\zeta_{ij})^{n_{ij}^B \, \nu_B}} \, . \tag{17}$$

From (17) it is possible to obtain another expression for k_p :

$$K_p = \Pi \, (\zeta_{ij})^{(\nu_C \, n_{ij}^C + \nu_D \, n_{ij}^D + \ldots - \nu_A \, n_{ij}^A - \nu_B \, n_{ij}^A - \ldots \,)} \, , \tag{18}$$

where the product holds for the nine sub-types of $C_i - C_j$ bonds, set out in Table 1, i.e. for vapours, suffices i, j $(i \leqslant j)$: are:

$$i = 1, 2, 3, 4; \quad j = 2, 3, 4.$$

The values of the quantity ζ_{ij} , calculated according to (16), for some temperatures are given in Table 10.

8. The Calculation of other Physico-chemical Quantities by the First Method (Density and Boiling Point)

The density d_4^{20} can be calculated from the equation

$$d_4^{20} = \frac{M}{V_M^{20}} = \frac{M}{\sum\limits_{i \leqslant j = 1}^{4} n_{ij} V_{ij}^{20}} \, , \tag{19}$$

where M is the molecular weight, and V_M^{20} is the molecular volume of an alkane at 20°C.

The comparison between experimental and calculated values is shown in Table 13. Similarly, d_4^{25} can be calculated from the equation

$$d_M^{25} = \frac{M}{V_M^{25}} = \frac{M}{\sum\limits_{i \leqslant j = 1}^{4} n_{ij} V_{ij}^{25}} \, . \tag{20}$$

The comparison of experimental and calculated values is

shown in Fig. 8. The values of V^{20}_{ij} and V^{25}_{ij} are given in Table 2.

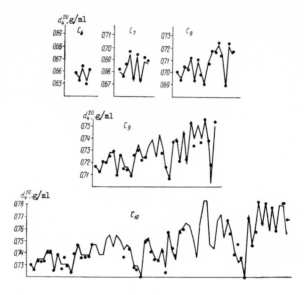

Fig. 8

Values of d^{20}_4 for the liquid alkanes $C_6 - C_{10}$, experimental from data of [49, 50] (points) and calculated according to equation (19) (lines)

Series of investigations on alkanes, as in Fig.2

The boiling point (t_{boil}) can be calculated from the equation

$$t_{boil\ p} = \frac{\lambda^\circ}{b - \lg p} - 273.16 = \frac{\sum\limits_{i \leqslant j = 1}^{4} n_{ij}\,\lambda_{ij}}{\sum\limits_{i \leqslant j = 1}^{4} n_{ij}b_{ij} - \lg p} - 273.16, \quad (21)$$

obtained as a consequence of equations (7), (4d) and (4e). The quantities λ_{ij} and b_{ij} for different temperature ranges were given above. The comparison of the experimental and calculated values of t_{boil} for alkanes at normal pressure ($p = 760$ mm mercury) is shown in Tables 18 and 19 and in Fig.9. The isomeric effect on boiling points is given

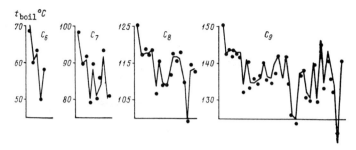

Fig. 9

Values of the normal boiling points for alkanes
$C_6 - C_9$, experimental from data of [49, 50]
(points) and calculated according to equation
(21) (lines)

Series of investigations on alkanes, as in Fig.2

basically by calculation. It is evident from formula (21)
that it is possible also to calculate t_{boil} for any other
vapour pressure.

9. Some Problems that Arise in the Mass Calculation of Physico-chemical Properties of Higher Alkanes by the First Method

The method (first) described above of calculating the
physico-chemical properties of alkanes has been used in
recent years for the calculation of many physico-chemical
properties of alkanes, of both those investigated experimentally and those uninvestigated. Good agreement of the
calculated and experimental values for the investigated hydrocarbons and successful forecasts of the physico-chemical properties of hydrocarbons of the different classes achieved
with the help of this method make the rapid calculation of a
series of physico-chemical properties for hundreds and thous-
ands of the higher hydrocarbons which have not been investigated experimentally completely possible.

One of the difficulties that arise in the mass calculation
of the physico-chemical properties of the higher hydrocarbons
$(C_{11}-C_{20})$ is the rapid increase in the number of isomers with
the growth in the number of carbon atoms. Thus, for example,

whilst for the alkane C_8 there are 18 isomers, yet for the
alkane C_{12} there are already 355 and for the alkane C_{20} ,
366,319. Direct calculation of the physico-chemical properties of the alkanes C_{20} according to the formulae of the
structure of all their isomers would demand the formation of
366,319 structural formulae and the corresponding equation
for the calculation, which is too difficult a task. Furthermore, to the degree of approximation to which the mathematical scheme of the first method of calculation is designed,
the calculation of the physico-chemical properties for each
isomer is essentially unnecessary. This is because the
physico-chemical properties of isomers of different structure
but possessing identical values of all the numbers n_{ij} , i.e.
identical distribution of the C—C bonds according to forms
(sub-types), are obtained in the calculation by the first
method by means of identities; this is approximately in
accordance with the experimental data. For example, for the
isomeric octanes, 3-methylheptane and 4-methylheptane, the
distribution of the seven C—C bonds according to the forms
is identical, as is easily seen from the structural formulae
of their carbon skeletons:

1)
$$C_1—C_2—C_3—C_2—C_2—C_2—C_1$$
$$\searrow$$
$$C_1$$
,

2)
$$C_1—C_2—C_2—C_3—C_2—C_3—C_1$$
$$\swarrow$$
$$C_1$$
.

In both cases the numbers n_{ij} equal: $n_{12} = 2$, $n_{13} = 1$, $n_{14} = 0$,
$n_{22} = 2$, $n_{23} = 2$, $n_{24} = 0$, $n_{33} = 0$, $n_{34} = 0$, $n_{44} = 0$. Consequently
equation (4) for the calculation of the physico-chemical
quantities P isomers will be

$$P = 2P_{12} + P_{13} + 2P_{22} + 2P_{23}$$

and the values obtained by calculation of the physico-chemical
quantities for both isomers will coincide.

Experimental data approximately correspond to this development of theory. The values of the physico-chemical quantities
for the isomers 2-methylheptane and 4-methylheptane, measured
experimentally, are very close.

Consequently, by the first method of calculation the isomeric alkanes with a given number of carbon atoms n are

divided into several groups, such that for each group of alkanes the numbers n_{ij} will be identical, and the value of any property, obtained by calculation from equation (4), will be identical for all the isomeric alkanes of the group.

The problem arises how to determine the number of groups into which the isomeric alkanes with a given number n of carbon atoms divide, and the value of the numbers n_{ij} for each group. Then it is sufficient to complete the calculation of the physico-chemical properties not for each alkane separately but only for each group with known values of the numbers n_{ij} for the given group and with values of the constants P_{ij} determined earlier from experimental data on the lower alkanes.

The problem set out above of splitting the alkanes with a given number of carbon atoms into the specified groups is solved in two stages. First of all we divide all the alkanes C into broader groups such that they are characterized by the fact that any alkane of the specific group possesses the very same number of carbon atoms, primary (k_1), secondary (k_2), tertiary (k_3) and quaternary (k_4). Secondly, these broader groups with the given distribution of the overall number of carbon atoms, n, into the numbers k_1, k_2, k_3, and k_4, are divided into groups such that each alkane possesses the very same number n_{ij} of bonds of each form.

We will call the above mentioned broader groups with specific values of the numbers k_1, k_2, k_3, k_4 for each alkane in the family 'the k_i groups'. The smaller groups with specific values of the numbers n_{ij} for each alkane of the group will be called 'the n_{ij} groups'.

10. The Determination of the 'k_i -groups' and the 'n_{ij} -groups' Into Which Alkanes With a Given Number of Carbon Atoms are Divided

Let us look at the alkanes C_n, i.e. those containing n carbon atoms. In order to solve the question of how many k_i groups to divide the alkanes C_n into, it is necessary to decide what the numbers k_1, k_2, k_3, k_4 of the primary, secondary, tertiary and quaternary carbon atoms can be for a given overall number of carbon atoms in the alkane. This question can be solved starting from two equations:

$$n = k_1 + k_2 + k_3 + k_4. \qquad (22)$$

$$n - 1 = \frac{1}{2} k_1 + k_2 + \frac{3}{2} k_3 + 2k_4. \tag{23}$$

The first equation is self-explanatory, the second is obtained if we separate the C—C bonds into carbon atoms. Then at C_1 , there will be half a C—C bond; at C_2 one C—C bond; at C_3 , $1\frac{1}{2}$ C—C bond; at C_4 two C—C bonds, and the overall number of C—C bonds in the alkane will be $n - 1$.

From equation (21) we obtain

$$n = k_2 + 2k_3 + 3k_4 + 2, \tag{24}$$

$$k_1 = k_3 + 2k_4 + 2. \tag{25}$$

Equation (25) shows that k_1 can be defined simply by k_3 and k_4 . In this way, the problem of establishing the 'k_1-group' for a given n boils down to the determination of the possible values of k_2, k_3, k_4. These values are determined as the integral positive solutions of equation (24). Consequently, all the 'k_1-groups' for a given n are determined by a system of integral positive solutions of equation (24). Methods of obtaining integral solutions of equations of type (24) are known [52, 53] and the solution does not present difficulty.

In this way, the problem of determining the 'k_1-groups' for a given n can be considered solved.

Consequently, for a given n it is possible to determine the number of carbon atoms, primary k_1, secondary k_2, tertiary k_3 and quaternary k_4, encountered in the corresponding 'k_1-groups' of alkanes with n carbon atoms.

We will now choose one of these groups, for which the numbers k_1, k_2, k_3 and k_4 are considered known, and we will raise the question into what 'n_{ij}-groups' it divides. In other words, what can the numbers n_{ij} be for alkanes with a known overall number n of carbon atoms and with given numbers k_1, k_2, k_3, k_4, of primary, secondary, tertiary and quaternary atoms, respectively.

This question can be solved in the following way. It is easily seen that the overall number of 'valencies' used by the C_i atoms in the C—C bonds is equal to ik_i , that the number of valencies used by the C_i atom in the $C_i - C_j$ bond $(i \neq j)$ is equal to unity, but in the C_i—C_i bond is equal to two. From these considerations, we can write down a system of equations:

$$2n_{11} + n_{12} + n_{13} + n_{14} = k_1,$$
$$n_{12} + 2n_{22} + n_{23} + n_{24} = 2k_2,$$
$$n_{13} + n_{23} + 2n_{33} + n_{34} = 3k_3, \qquad (26)$$
$$n_{14} + n_{24} + n_{34} + 2n_{44} = 4k_4.$$

For all alkanes except ethane, $n_{11} = 0$; therefore we can substitute, for all alkanes except ethane, $n_{11} = 0$ in system (26). System (26) determines all the values of n_{ij} which can correspond to an alkane with a given number n of carbon atoms and given values k_1, k_2, k_3, and k_4 of the primary, secondary, tertiary and quaternary carbon atoms. However, it is easily seen that in the system of solutions of system (26) there are spare solutions, i.e. those which are not encountered in a single alkane. Actually, system (26) includes systems of solutions which represent the division of the C_i—C_j bonds into the numbers n_{ij} , but which refer not to a single molecule of alkane but to two or several molecules of hydrocarbons which are not bonded together. To demonstrate this it is evidently sufficient to show what happens if there is one similar system of solutions of equations (26).

Take, for example, the numbers k_1, k_2, k_3, k_4 as: $k_1 = 13$, $k_2 = 2$, $k_3 = 3$, $k_4 = 4$. They satisfy equations (24) and (25).

The system of solutions:

$$\begin{aligned}
n_{12} &= 2, \quad n_{22} = 1, \quad n_{33} = 3, \\
n_{13} &= 3, \quad n_{23} = 0, \quad n_{34} = 0, \qquad (27) \\
n_{14} &= 8, \quad n_{24} = 0, \quad n_{44} = 4
\end{aligned}$$

satisfies equations (26). It is easily seen that this system of solutions corresponds to the division of the bond into three hydrocarbon molecules, not bonded with one another - octamethylcyclobutane, 1,2,3-trimethylcyclopropane and n-butane. Actually, the carbon skeletons of these molecules will be

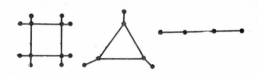

From these schemes it is easily seen that the numbers n_{ij} (27), substituted above and satisfying equations (26), give the division of the C—C bonds into these three isolated molecules.

It can be shown that it is impossible to build any molecule of alkane in which the division of the C_i—C_j bonds into the numbers n_{ij} is expressed by the numbers in (27). In this way, among the solutions of the system of equations in (26) there are extra ones which do not refer to alkanes.

To exclude the superfluous solutions of system (26) it is necessary to impose on its solutions additional conditions which would exclude the division of the $C_i — C_j$ bonds into the numbers n_{ij} which refer to the cyclic hydrocarbons.

These conditions are easily formulated, if it is noted that the rings could be formed in several different ways. It is obvious that the rings could include:

a) only secondary carbon atoms;

b) only tertiary carbon atoms;

c) only quaternary carbon atoms;

d) secondary and tertiary carbon atoms;

e) secondary and quaternary carbon atoms;

f) tertiary and quaternary carbon atoms;

g) secondary, tertiary and quaternary carbon atoms.

If S atoms form one or several rings, then the number of bonds between them will satisfy the condition

$$t > S - 1. \qquad (28)$$

If S atoms do not form a single ring then

$$t \leqslant S - 1. \tag{29}$$

Starting from this, it is easy to formulate the conditions in which it is impossible to form rings by any of the means set out in items a)-g) above. For example, so that no rings will be formed containing only secondary atoms (item a)) (based on condition (29)) it is necessary to fulfil the condition

$$n_{22} \leqslant k_2 - 1.$$

Actually in this case n_{22}, the number of $C_2 - C_2$ bonds, should be, according to condition (29), less than or equal to the number of C_2 atoms less unity, i.e. less than or equal to $k_2 - 1$. Similarly, conditions can be obtained that exclude the possibility of the formation of rings of the other types set out in items b)-f) above. A condition that would exclude the possibility of the formation of rings of the type g) occurring superfluously in system (26) is not necessary, since it is easily shown that this condition is already contained in equations (24)-(26).

The complete system of conditions, excluding solutions of equations (26), that refer not to alkane molecules, but to a collection of moleculaes of alkanes and cyclic compounds would be

$$
\begin{aligned}
n_{22} &\leqslant k_2 - 1, \\
n_{33} &\leqslant k_3 - 1, \\
n_{44} &\leqslant k_4 - 1, \\
n_{22} + n_{23} + n_{33} &\leqslant k_3 + k_2 - 1, \\
n_{22} + n_{24} + n_{44} &\leqslant k_4 + k_2 - 1, \\
n_{33} + n_{34} + n_{44} &\leqslant k_4 + k_3 - 1.
\end{aligned}
\tag{30}
$$

System (26) together with system (30) gives all the possibilities of dividing the $C_i - C_j$ bonds into the numbers n_{ij}, referred to alkanes. It is obvious that for given k_1, k_2, k_3 and k_4, i.e. for given 'k_i-groups' of alkanes, the solutions of the system of equations (26) and (30) (positive and integral) give all possible divisions of $n - 1$ $C_i - C_j$ bonds in the alkane into the numbers n_{ij}, i.e. they determine all the 'n_{ij}-groups' or all the sets of coefficients n in the equation

$$P = \sum_{i<j=1}^{4} n_{ij}P_{ij}, \tag{4}$$

which hold for alkanes with given n and given k_1, k_2, k_3, k_4..

In this way, for given n we can first calculate all possible combinations of the numbers k_1, k_2, k_3, k_4 from (24) and (25), and then for each of the combinations of the numbers k_1, k_2, k_3, k_4 we calculate from (26) and (27) all the possible combinations of the numbers n_{ij} and set up all possible equations (4) for the determination of the property P of all the 'n_{ij} -groups' of alkanes. For all alkanes of a given 'n_{ij} - group', the calculated value of the property P is the same.

By this means, values of the property P can be obtained for the 'n_{ij} -groups' of alkanes, without constructing their structural formulae, being based only on the systems of equations (24)-(26) and (30). The specified method, within the limits of accuracy of the assumption put forward on the basis of equation (4), gives the possibility of finding out all possible different values of the property P for alkanes with a given number n of carbon atoms.

11. Some Physico-chemical Properties of the C_{11} Alkanes, Calculated by the First Method

The method of calculation of the division of the $C_i - C_j$ bonds into the numbers n_{ij} was carried out [43] for the C_{11} hydrocarbons. All possible divisions of the eleven carbon atoms into primary, secondary, tertiary and quaternary, occurring in the C_{11} alkanes were calculated. For the values obtained of the quantities k_1, k_2, k_3 and k_4 for each possible combination of those values, the possible divisions of the $C_i - C_j$ bonds into the quantities n_{ij} were calculated according to equation (26) and the inequality (30). For each possible division of the $C - C$ bonds into the quantities n_{ij} , some physico-chemical properties of the corresponding groups of alkanes were calculated using the constants for the corresponding physico-chemical properties, given above in the Tables. The results of these calculations are given in Table 20. In it are given values of the quantities n_{ij} for each 'n_{ij} -group' of the C_{11} alkanes and the values calculated by the method described above of some physico-chemical properties for alkanes of all groups. For the known division of the $C_i - C_j$ bonds into the quantities n_{ij} it is not difficult

to construct the carbon skeletons of hydrocarbons appropriate
to each group. For the example of the C_{11} alkanes, it is seen
that the number of ' n_{ij} -groups' is considerably less than the
number of isomers of the C_{11} alkanes. For the C_{11} alkanes there
are 159 isomers which group themselves into only 83 groups.

CHAPTER II

HOMOLOGOUS RULES IN THE SERIES OF BRANCHED ALKANES. THE SECOND METHOD OF CALCULATING THE PHYSICO-CHEMICAL PROPERTIES OF ALKANES

1. The Nature of the Method

Earlier, equation (4) was given, reproducing the link between a certain property P of the isomeric alkanes and the quantities n_{ij} of the $C_i - C_j$ bonds in the alkane, where the indices i, j signify whether the C atoms, which form the chemical bonds in the alkane molecule, are primary, secondary, tertiary or quaternary $(i, j = 1, 2, 3, 4)$. This equation for an arbitrary branched alkane with n atoms of carbon takes the form:-

$$P_n = \sum_{i \leqslant j=1}^{4} n_{ij}P_{ij} = n_{12}P_{12} + n_{13}P_{13} + n_{14}P_{14} + n_{22}P_{22} + n_{23}P_{23} + \\ + n_{24}P_{24} + n_{33}P_{33} + n_{34}P_{34} + n_{44}P_{44}, \tag{4}$$

where P_{ij} are certain constants, obtained from experimental data.

Considering the two equations in [31] connecting the overall number of carbon atoms n in the alkane with the quantities n_{ij} of the $C_i - C_j$ bonds of different forms:

$$n - 1 = n_{12} + n_{13} + n_{14} + n_{22} + n_{23} + n_{24} + n_{33} + n_{34} + n_{44} \tag{31}$$

and

$$+ \frac{7}{12} n_{34} + \frac{1}{2} n_{44}, \tag{32}$$

equation can be changed [31] to the form

$$P_n = 2P_{12} + (n-3) \ P_{22} + \sum_{i \leqslant j=1}^{4} n_{ij}G_{ij}, \tag{33}$$

where $G_{13} = G_{22} = 0$ and the remaining G_{ij} are connected with the constants P_{ij} by the following equations:

$$G_{13} = P_{13} - \frac{2}{3}P_{12} - \frac{1}{3}P_{22}; \qquad G_{24} = P_{24} + \frac{1}{2}P_{12} - \frac{3}{2}P_{22},$$

$$G_{14} = P_{14} - \frac{1}{2}P_{12} - \frac{1}{2}P_{22}, \qquad G_{33} = P_{33} + \frac{2}{3}P_{12} - \frac{5}{3}P_{22},$$

$$G_{23} = P_{23} + \frac{1}{3}P_{12} - \frac{4}{3}P_{22}, \qquad G_{34} = P_{34} + \frac{5}{6}P_{12} - \frac{11}{6}P_{22}. \qquad (34)$$

$$G_{44} = P_{44} + P_{12} - 2P_{22}.$$

For a normal alkane with the same number, n, of carbon atoms, it is evident that

$$P_{n,\ \text{norm}} = 2P_{12} + (n-3)P_{22}, \qquad (35)$$

since in this case all n_{ij}, apart from n_{12} and n_{22}, are equal to zero.

Combining equations (33) and (35), we can write

$$P_{n,\ \text{branched}} = P_{n,\ \text{norm}} + \sum_{i \leqslant j=1}^{4} n_{ij}G_{ij} = 2P_{12} + (n-3)P_{22} + \Delta, \quad (36)$$

where

$$\Delta = \sum_{i \leqslant j=1}^{4} n_{ij}G_{ij}.$$

According to [31], there exist groups of alkanes such that, for a change in n, Δ remains approximately constant for all members of the same group. The division of alkanes into such groups is given for the simplest alkanes in Table 11 together with the expression Δ in terms of G_{ij}. If we enumerate these groups in some order (Table 11, column 1), then for the mth group we would get

$$P_n^m = 2P_{12} - 3P_{22} + \Delta^m + nP_{22} = a^m + \beta n, \qquad (37)$$

where a^m is a constant for the mth group of alkanes, but $\beta = P_{22}$ in accordance with the ideas developed above should be identical for all groups of alkanes.

Consequently, if the property P obeys equation (4), then for each of the homologous groups of alkanes given in the table, within the confines of this group the property P will change linearly with increase in n, because the coefficient β of the corresponding straight lines will be identical for all groups, but for constant a^m in terms of Δ^m will change from group to group. In this way the rules are well-known for the n-alkanes (linear variation of some properties with respect to n) should be completely analogous to those for each group of alkanes given in Table 11, if our theoretical deductions are correct. The given predictions from theory agree well with experiment (see below).

Actually, in each of the homologous groups of alkanes listed above, the properties vary linearly with n. Apparently these rules, first discovered and explained in the reports [31], [36] and [38], extend the ideas on the laws obeyed by physical-chemical properties in homologous series of hydrocarbons and, in our opinion, can be considered as a development of the physico-chemical set of ideas on homologous, formulated earlier by Yu. A. Zhdanov [48]. It is obvious that the linear variations established earlier for specified physico-chemical properties of hydrocarbons of each homologous group can be used directly, by means of constants a^m and β, for the calculations of the corresponding magnitudes for the higher alkanes belonging to the given group.

The reduction and linear graphical extrapolation for the higher hydrocarbons belonging to the given homologous group can be extremely easy and convenient, if data are available on some of the lower hydrocarbons of the same group.

Here it should be observed that, for a given physico-chemical quantity, the constant β should be identical for all groups of alkanes if the ideas considered are completely accurate. However, as can be seen from Figs. 10-13, the slopes of the straight lines

$$P_n^m = a^m + \beta\, n, \qquad (37)$$

defined by the constant β for different groups of alkanes are slightly different for the series of cases, which shows that theory is not completely exact, but accurate to a certain approximation (in fact, quite good).

Consequently, if the constant β is determined from experimental data for each group of alkanes separately, then the values of β for the different groups will be slightly different.

In connexion with this, equation (37) can be written in the form

$$P_n^m = \alpha_p^m + \beta_p^m\, n, \qquad (38)$$

where β^m is very approximate for all groups, but all of them are slightly different for the different groups, which is denoted by the index m. The calculation, according to equation (38), of the quantities V, R, L (or λ), B (or b), log p, ΔH (at.), ΔH (el.), ΔH (comb.), ΔZ (el.) represents a new method of calculation of all the physico-chemical constants for the higher alkanes of a given group (for example, the mth) from the constants α^m and β^m, obtained from experimental data on the lower alkanes of that group.

2. Molecular Volumes

For the molecular volume of alkanes of the mth group for a definite specified temperature, equation (38) takes the form

$$V_n^m = \alpha_v^m + \beta_v^m\, n. \qquad (39)$$

The constants α_v^m and β_v^m for the different groups, calculated from experimental data are given in Table 12. A comparison of the experimental values of the molecular volumes with those calculated according to (39) for alkanes of different groups is shown in Table 21. The linear type variation of V_n^m with n in each group, as is also expected from theory, is illustrated in Fig. 10, derived from experimental data.

3. Latent Heats of Vaporization

The diagram showing the linear variation of the latent heat of vaporization $L_n^{0\,m}$ or of the quantity equivalent to it $\lambda_n^{0\,m}$ with the quantity n for alkanes of the mth group is shown in Fig. 11, based on the initial values λ^0, obtained from experimental values of vapour pressures of alkanes. From the diagram it is evident that linear variations of the type

$$\lambda_n^{0\,m} = \alpha_\lambda^m + \beta_\lambda^m n \qquad (40)$$

D

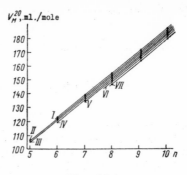

Fig. 10

Change in molecular volumes V_M^{20} with
change in the number of carbon atoms n
in a molecule, for alkanes if different groups

I. 2,2-dimethylalkanes; II. 2-methylalkanes; straight
line, III. n-alkanes; IV. 3-methylalkanes; V. 3,3-
dimethylalkanes; VI. 3,4-dimethylalkanes; VII. 2,3,3-
trimethylalkanes

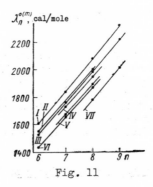

Fig. 11

Change in λ_n^{0m} with change in the number
of carbon atoms in a molecule for alkanes
of different groups over the temperature
range 40–80°C

I. n-alkanes; II. 3-methylalkanes; III. 2-methylal-
kanes; IV. 2,3-dimethylalkanes; V. 3-ethylalkanes;
VI. 2,2-dimethylalkanes; VII. 2,2, $(n-1)$-trimethyl-
alkanes

are fulfilled satisfactorily for alkanes of each group. The values α_λ^m and β_λ^m for certain groups of alkanes are given in Table 12.

4. Heats of Combusion, Thermodynamic Potentials and other Physico-chemical Quantities for Alkanes

In Fig. 12, for the example ΔH (el. gas), it is shown to what extent equation (38) (linear variation with n) is verified for specified physico-chemical quantities with respect

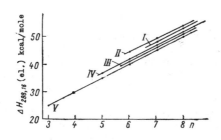

Fig. 12

Change in ΔH° (el.gas) at $T = 298.16^\circ$ with change in the number of carbon atoms in a molecule for alkanes of different groups

I. 2,(n-1)-dimethylalkanes; 2,2-dimethylalkanes;
III. 3-methylalkanes; IV. 2-methylalkanes;
V. n-alkanes

to alkanes of certain groups, by means of experimental data. From Fig. 12, it is evident that experimental data really do display linear variations predicted by theory which evidently can be used for the calculation of the properties of the higher hydrocarbons of a given group from the properties of the lower hydrocarbons of the given group, in a similar way to that which was carried out for molecular volumes.

The values α_H^m and β_H^m for the calculation of $\Delta H_{el.}^0$ for alkanes of certain homologous groups are shown in Table 12.

5. Vapour Pressure

Equation (38) for the logarithm of the saturated vapour pressure of liquid alkanes C_nH_{2n+2}, belonging to the m th group possesses the form

$$\log p_n^m = 2\pi_{12} - 3\pi_{22} + \Delta_p^m + \pi_{22}\, n = a_p^m + \beta_p^m\, n, \qquad (41)$$

where the symbol π_{ij} was explained above; Δ_p^m is the change in the logarithm of the vapour pressure during isomerization of the alkane C_nH_{2n+2} of a given group into a normal alkane C_nH_{2n+2} (Δ according to theory is constant for a given group).

In this way from the stated theoretical considerations it follows that there is a linear variation of the logarithm of the vapour pressure with the number of carbon atoms for alkanes of a given group. Theory demands that the slope of the corresponding straight lines for different groups should be constant (that is, that π_{22} should be constant). The agreement of theory with practice is shown in Fig. 13; it is completely satisfactory and gives a new method of calculation of the vapour pressures of higher alkanes of a given group from the vapour pressure of the lower alkanes of that group. The values of a_p^m and β_p^m for the calculation of the logarithms of the vapour pressure for certain groups of alkanes for the temperature range 130-170°C, are shown in Table 12.

6. Certain Specialized Rules

Vapour pressures. The logarithms of the vapour pressures for two alkanes with the same number of carbon atoms, of which one belongs to the m th group and the other the k th group, starting from equations (37) and (41), can be expressed in the form

$$\log p_n^m = 2\pi_{12} - 3\pi_{22} + \Delta_p^m + \pi_{22}\, n,$$
$$\log p_n^k = 2\pi_{12} - 3\pi_{22} + \Delta_p^k + \pi_{22}\, n. \qquad (42)$$

from this

$$\log \frac{p_n^m}{p_n^k} = \Delta_p^m - \Delta_p^k. \qquad (43)$$

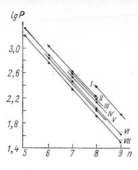

Fig. 13

Change in the logarithm of the vapour
pressure with change in the number of
carbon atoms in a molecule, for alkanes
of different groups

I. 2,2,(n-1)-trimethylalkanes; II. 2,2-dimethylalkanes;
III. 2,(n-1)-dimethylalkanes; IV. 3,3-dimethylalkanes;
V. 3-methylalkanes; VI. 2-methylalkanes; VII. *n*-alkanes

The first part (43) does not vary with n , consequently

$$\log \frac{p_n^m}{p_n^k} = \Delta_p^{m,k} = \text{const},\qquad(44)$$

or

$$\frac{p_n^m}{p_n^k} = C,\qquad(45)$$

where C is a constant.

In this way the ratio of the vapour pressures of two alkanes, containing the same number of atoms and belonging to
different groups, at a given temperature is of constant
magnitude and does not vary with the number of carbon atoms.
Consequently, the curve

$$p_n^m = f^m(n)\qquad(46)$$

for the mth group of alkanes can be obtained from the curve

$$p_n^k = f^k(n)\qquad(47)$$

for the kth group of alkanes by multiplication by the constant C , for the determination of which it is sufficient to
know the vapour pressure of only one alkane of the mth
group, if $p_n^k = f^k(n)$ is known.

Equilibrium constants of the isomerization reaction of
alkanes. For the isomerization reaction of the alkane
C_nH_{2n+2} of the mth group into the alkane C_nH_{2n+2} of the kth
group, we will have

$$RT \ln K_p = \Delta Z_n^{0,\,m} - \Delta Z_n^{0,\,k}.\qquad(48)$$

The first part in the basic equation (48) does not vary
with n and equals

$$\Delta_z^m - \Delta_z^k.$$

Thence

$$RT \ln K_p = \Delta_z^m - \Delta_z^k = C_z^{m,\,k},$$

that is, the equilibrium constant for the isomerization rea-
tion of a hydrocarbon of the mth group into a hydrocarbon

of the k the group at any given temperature is the same for any n, i.e. it does not vary with the number of carbon atoms of the alkane being isomerized.

7. Heats of Crystallization

As we will see below, in considering the laws obeyed by heats of crystallization, complications arise connected with the presence of the solid phase, which are absent when the properties of the gaseous or liquid phases are considered.

The point is that during crystallization various crystalline modifications can arise which differ either in the packing of the molecules in the crystalline lattice or in the geometrical form of the same molecule (rotational isomerizm) in the crystal.

It is natural that simple laws connecting the heat of crystallization with the number of carbon atoms in a molecule can be found only by comparing the heat of crystallization of a series of alkanes in one and the same crystalline modification. This occurs in the consideration of the laws of heats of crystallization of n-alkanes, since n-alkanes with an even and odd number of carbon atoms in the molecule and also higher and lower alkanes apparently crystallize into various crystalline modifications.

In Fig. 14, can be seen a graph of a change in the temperature of crystallization of n-alkanes with respect to the number of carbon atoms in a molecule. From the diagram it is evident that the temperature of crystallization of n-alkanes, with even and odd number of carbon atoms, gives two different smooth curves, which shows that crystalline modifications for n-alkanes with even and odd number of carbon atoms are different. A similar picture, although less clearly expressed because of the small number of experimental data, is obtained for the 2-methylalkanes. From this it follows that since crystalline modifications for alkanes with even and odd number of carbon atoms are different then the law connecting heat of crystallization and the number of carbon atoms in a molecule of alkane should be sought separately for alkanes with even and odd numbers of carbon atoms.

An examination of each of the groups of n-alkanes (with even n and odd n) shows that, in each of these groups during crystallization of the liquid alkanes, there arise dis-

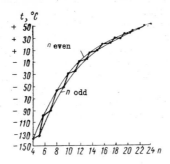

Fig. 14

The variation of t_{cryst} with the
number of carbon atoms in a molecule for n-alkanes

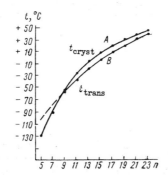

Fig. 15

The variation of t_{cryst} and t_{trans}
(n odd with respect to n for n-
alkanes)

similar crystalline modifications for alkanes differing in
the number of carbon atoms per molecule.

Let us consider first the alkanes with an odd number of
carbon atoms, beginning with n-pentane. For the two lower

alkanes with odd n (n-pentane and n-heptane) near the temperature of crystallization, a point is not found where the
solid phase is changed into another crystalline modification.
For alkanes with odd $n \gg 9$, a little below the temperature
of crystallization is the transition temperature of the crystalline modification, which arises during crystallization
(we will call this modification A) into another crystalline
modification (we will call this modification B). In Fig. 15,
graphs are given of the change in temperature of crystalliza-
tion (t cryst) and transition temperature (t_{trans}) for n-alkanes
with odd n .

If the heat of crystallization of a liquid in modification
A is denoted by L_A and the heat of transition of form A into
form B is denoted by L_{AB} , then the heat of crystallization
of a liquid immediately into form B^* is

$$L_B = L_A + L_{AB}. \qquad (50)$$

It can be seen that, for alkanes with $n \geqslant 9$ for odd n , a
linear variation of L_A and L_B with n is to be expected,
provided these linear variations, generally speaking, can be
different

$$L_A = \alpha_A + \beta_A n, \qquad (51)$$

$$L_B = \alpha_B + \beta_B n. \qquad (52)$$

In Fig. 16 it is shown that the specified linear variations
really do hold for $n \gg 9$. From the diagram it can be seen
that the heats of crystallization observed directly during
the crystallization of the liquids n-pentane and n-heptane
($n < 9$) well satisfy the straight line L_B (n), which illus-
trates the fact that n-pentane and n-heptane crystallize
into form B and not into form A.

In this way, it is possible to establish the correspondence
between crystalline modifications into which the lower and
higher n-alkanes with odd n are crystallized. For each of
the crystalline forms, L_A and L_B vary linearly with n,
which is evident from Fig. 16 and Table 23.

---

*We shall neglect here the small number of cases containing specific heats of differ-
ent phases, since t_{cryst} and t_{trans} are close.

For n-alkanes with odd n , the experimental values of L_A and L_B for $n \geqslant 20$ are probably very inexact, since the measurements were conducted with compounds of an unknown

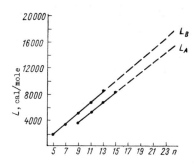

Fig. 16

The variation of the heats of
crystallization of **n**-alkanes
(n odd) with the number n ,
for crystalline modifications
A and *B*

degree of purity. We consider the values, calculated according to equations (51) and (52) to be more reliable. There is also some doubt about the value of L_A for n-heptadecane, since for this hydrocarbon L_{AB} (and consequently L_B) was not determined, but the experimental value is nearer to the calculated L_B than to the calculated L_A . Probably, the quantity measured experimentally is an average between L_A and L_B or a value near to L_B .

Let us look now at n-alkanes with even n . For these alkanes in the range $5 < n < 20$, transition points of the crystalline modification arising during the crystallization of a liquid into another crystalline modification were not found. For $n < 5$ or $n > 20$ such transition points (t_{trans}) are given for which limits t_{trans} are a little less than t_{cryst} (Fig. 17).

From Fig. 17 for $5 < n < 20$ it would be expected that all liquid n-alkanes with even n crystallize into one and the

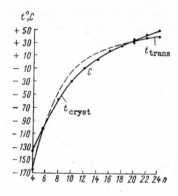

Fig. 17

The variation of t_{cryst} and t_{trans}
of n-alkanes (n even) with n

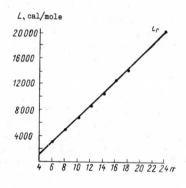

Fig. 18

The variation of the heat of
crystallization of n-alkanes
(n even) with the number n,
for crystalline modification

same crystalline modification (we will call this modification
C). Corresponding to this modification, the heat of

crystallization L_C should vary linearly with n

$$L_C = a_c + \beta_c n. \tag{53}$$

This variation does really occur, as is shown in Fig. 18. For higher alkanes, with even $n > 20$, which can occur in the solid phase in two crystalline modifications (we will call the second of these, modification D), the experimental values [49] of L_C and L_D are apparently quite inaccurate, since they were all obtained for compounds of an unknown degree of purity and do not show a regular variation, as is seen from Fig. 5. Therefore, values of heat of crystallization for even $n > 20$ are not given in Table 23.

For n-butane, $L(\text{cryst}) + L(\text{trans})$ lie satisfactorily on the straight line L_C, so that n-butane lower than t_{trans} occurs, apparently, in modification C.

In Table 22 are given the value of a_c and β_c, calculated from experimental data. In Table 23 experimental values are compared with calculated ones. For $n > 20$ we consider the calculated values of L_C to be more reliable than the experimental values of $L(\text{cryst}) + L(\text{trans})$, which should apparently be interpreted as the value of L_C.

8. The Calculation of Other Physico-chemical Quantities by the Second Method (Density, Boiling Point)

Besides the physico-chemical quantities calculated above, the second method of calculation can be used indirectly for the calculation of the density and boiling points of alkanes.

Density. For the calculation of the density of alkanes of the mth group, starting from equation (19), we get for the alkane C_nH_{2n+2}:

$$d_n^m = \frac{M_n}{V_n^m}, \tag{54}$$

where d_n^m is the density, M_n is the molecular weight, V_n^m is the molecular volume of the alkane C_nH_{2n+2} belonging to the mth group.

By considering that

$$M_n = 2M_{CH_3} + (n - 2) M_{CH_2}, \qquad (55)$$

where M_{CH_3} and M_{CH_2} are the molecular weights of the groups CH_3 and CH_2, equal to 15.084 and 14.026 respectively, we obtain, from equation (54),

$$d_n^m = \frac{2.016 + 14.026\, n}{\alpha_v^m + \beta_v^m\, n}, \qquad (56)$$

where α_v^m and β_v^m are constants in equation (39) for molecular volume.

Having determined these constants from experimental values of d_n^m for hydrocarbons of a given m th group, we can then use them for the calculation of d_n^m of other hydrocarbons of the same m th group. For the calculations of density at 20° the constants α_v^m and β_v^m can be taken from Table 12.

Equation (56) possesses in general the form

$$d_n^m = \frac{\gamma + \delta n}{\alpha_v^{(m)} + \beta_v^{(m)} n}. \qquad (57)$$

By dividing this by β_v^m and performing a simple substitution, we can change it into another form

$$d_n^m = A^m + \frac{B^m}{n_0^m + n} \qquad (58)$$

with the constants A^m, B^m, n_0^m :

$$A^m = \frac{\delta}{\beta_v^m}, \quad B^m = \frac{\gamma}{\beta_v^m} - \frac{\delta \alpha_v^m}{(\beta_v^m)^2}, \quad n_0^m = \frac{\alpha_v^m}{\beta_v^m}. \qquad (59)$$

It is easy to see that, since, in equation (57), γ, δ and β_v according to theory should be constants for all groups of alkanes, then A^{ι} should be constant for all groups of alkane Experiment shows that this is not the case. All three constants A^m, B^m, n_0^m more or less change from group to group; however the form of equation (58) with the three empirically determined constants A^m, B^m, n_0^m depicts the experimental dat well, somewhat better than equation (57) with fixed values o γ and δ and two empirical constants α_v^m and β_v^m. In Fig. 19 and in Table 21, the experimental values of density are compared, for different groups of alkanes, with those calculate according to equations (56) and (58).

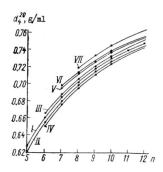

Fig. 19

Change in d_4^{20} with change in the
number of carbon atoms n in a
molecule for alkanes of different
groups

I. n-alkanes; II. 2-methylalkanes; III. 3-methylalkanes;
IV. 2,2-dimethylalkanes; V. 2,3-dimethylalkanes; VI. 3-
ethylalkanes; VII. 3,4-dimethylalkanes

As can be seen, the accuracy of the calculation according
to both equations is such that it is quite possible to extra-
polate values of density for the higher alkanes, containing
up to three carbon atoms more than those investigated experimentally in the given group. If there are too few accurate
experimental data for the reliable determination of the three
constants A^m , B^m and n_0^m or $n \gg n_0^m$, perhaps the simplified
relationship can be used

$$d_n^m = \overline{A}^m + \frac{\overline{B}^m}{n} , \qquad (60)$$

for which it is necessary to determine only two constants:
$\overline{A}^m$ and $\overline{B}^m$ from experimental data.

Boiling point. Using equation (37), we obtain λ^0 and b
for the m th group in a similar way to that described above
for a certain temperature T :

$$\lambda_{n, T}^0 = 2\lambda_{12, T} - 3\lambda_{22, T} + \Delta_{\lambda, T}^{n} + \lambda_{22, T} n,$$

$$b_{n, T} = 2b_{12, T} - 3b_{22, T} + \Delta_{b, T}^m + b_{22, T} n. \qquad (61)$$

From equation (21) we get

$$\log p_{n,\,T}^{m} = - \frac{2\lambda_{12,\,T} - 3\lambda_{22,\,T} + \Delta_{\lambda,\,T}^{m} + \lambda_{22,\,T}\,n}{T} + 2b_{12,\,T} - 3b_{22,\,T} + \qquad (62)$$
$$+ \Delta_{b,\,T}^{m} + b_{22,\,T}\,n.$$

It can be assumed from an analysis of the variation of λ_{ij} and b_{ij} with T, for the range 40-170°, that the following approximate equalities are correct to sufficient accuracy.

$$\lambda_{12,\,T} = \lambda_{12,\,0} = \text{const}, \quad b_{12,\,T} = b_{12,\,0} = \text{const},$$

$$\lambda_{22,\,T} = \lambda_{22,\,0} + \lambda_{22}' T, \quad b_{22,\,T} = b_{22,\,0} + \frac{b_{22}'}{T}, \qquad (63)$$

$$\Delta_{\lambda,\,T}^{m} = \Delta_{\lambda,\,0}^{m} + \Delta_{\lambda}^{m} T, \quad \Delta_{b,\,T}^{m} = \Delta_{b,\,0}^{m} + \frac{\Delta_{b}^{m}}{T}.$$

Then combining (63) and (62), we get

$$\log p_{n,\,T}^{m} = - \frac{2\lambda_{12,\,0} - 3\lambda_{22,\,0} + \Delta_{\lambda,\,0}^{m} - 3b_{22}' + \Delta_{b}^{m} + (\lambda_{22,\,0} + b_{22}')\,n}{T} + \qquad (64)$$
$$+ 2b_{12,\,0} - 3b_{22,\,0} + \Delta_{\lambda}^{m} + \Delta_{b,\,0}^{m} + (\lambda_{22}' + b_{22,\,0})\,n.$$

For $T = T_{n,\,\text{boil}}^{m}$ (boiling point of the alkane C_nH_{2n+2} of a given mth group) $p_{n,\,T} = 760$ mm mercury. Substituting these quantities in equation (64), we get

$$T_{n,\text{boil}}^{m} = \frac{2\lambda_{12,\,0} - 3\lambda_{22,\,0} + \Delta_{\lambda,\,0}^{m} - 3b_{22}' + \Delta_{b}^{m} + (\lambda_{22,\,0} + b_{22}')\,n}{2b_{12,\,0} - 3b_{22,\,0} + \Delta_{\lambda}^{m} + \Delta_{b,\,0}^{m} - \lg 760 + (\lambda_{22}' + b_{22,\,0})\,n}. \qquad (65)$$

This equation can be changed into the form

$$T_{n,\text{boil}}^{m} = T_{0}^{m} + \frac{C^{m}}{n_{0}^{m} + n} \qquad (66)$$

or

$$t_{n,\text{boil}}^{m} = t_{0}^{m} + \frac{C^{m}}{n_{0}^{m} + n}, \qquad (67)$$

where

$$T_0^m = \frac{\lambda_{22,0} + b'_{22}}{\lambda'_{22,0} + b_{22,0}}, \qquad t_0^m = T_0^m - 273.16,$$

$$C^m = \frac{2\lambda_{12,0} - 3\lambda_{22,0} + \Delta_{\lambda,0}^m + \Delta_b^m}{\lambda'_{22} + b_{22,0}} - $$

$$- \frac{(\lambda_{22,0} + b'_{22})(2b_{12,0} - 3b_{22,0} + \Delta_{b,0}^m + \Delta_\lambda^m - \lg 760)}{(\lambda'_{22} + b_{22,0})^2}, \qquad (68)$$

$$n_0^m = \frac{2b_{12,0} - 3b_{22,0} + \Delta_{b,0}^m + \Delta_\lambda^m - \lg 760}{\lambda'_{22} + b_{22,0}}.$$

In this way, the boiling point of alkanes of the mth group for a given pressure is described, to within the approximation in question, by the linear fractional function of n, similar to that for density.

The simplest means of using equation (67) in practice for the calculation of boiling points of the higher alkanes of a given group is as follows. Three constants t_0^m, C^m, n_0^m can be determined from experimental data for the investigated alkanes of a given group, and then their values are used for the calculation of other alkanes of the given group. In Fig.20

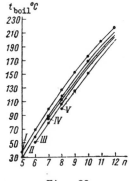

Fig. 20

Change in t_{boil} with change in the number of carbon atoms per molecule for alkanes of different groups

I. n-alkanes; II. 2-methylalkanes; III. 2,2-dimethylalkanes;
IV. 3,3-dimethylalkanes; V. 2,2,(n-1)-trimethylalkanes

and Table 24 are. given data, which permit an evaluation of the accuracy of such a calculation.

It is clear that, by the method indicated by equation (67), t_{boil} can be calculated for higher alkanes not only at normal but also at any other pressure from corresponding experimenta data for lower alkanes.

In those case when $n \gg n_0^m$ or there are too few data for the calculation of the three constants t_0^m, C^m, n_0^m , then the simplified equation can be used successfully

$$t_{n,\text{boil}}^m = \overline{t}_0^m + \frac{\overline{C}^m}{n} \tag{69}$$

with two constants $\overline{t}_0^m$, $\overline{C}^m$, obtained from experimental data.

CHAPTER III

THE CONNEXION BETWEEN DIFFERENT PHYSICO-CHEMICAL
PROPERTIES OF ALKANES OF VARIOUS HOMOLOGOUS
GROUPS. THE THIRD METHOD OF CALCULATION

1. The Nature of the Method. The Connexion Between Two Properties of one Homologous Group of Alkanes

As was shown earlier, there exists a linear relation between the value of a given physico-chemical property P of alkanes belonging to a definite homologous group and the number of carbon atoms n in a given alkane

$$P_n^m = a_p^m + \beta_p^m n, \qquad (38)$$

where a_p^m and β_p^m are constants for the given (m th) homologous group of alkanes.

It is easy to see that, if equation (38) is satisfied by two different properties P and Q in the given (m th) homologous group of alkanes, then there exists between these properties a linear variation of the form

$$P_n^m = AQ_n^m + B, \qquad (70)$$

where A and B are constants.

Actually if, besides the property P, another property Q satisfies an equation of the type (38):

$$Q_n^m = a_Q^m + \beta_Q^m n, \qquad (71)$$

then, from equations (38) and (71), we obtain

$$\frac{P_n^m - a_p^m}{Q_n^m - a_Q^m} = \frac{\beta_p^m}{\beta_Q^m}. \qquad (72)$$

E

53

Thence

$$P_n^m = \frac{\beta_p^m}{\beta_Q^m} Q_n^m + a_p^m - a_Q^m \frac{\beta_p^m}{\beta_Q^m} = AQ_n^m + B, \qquad (73)$$

where

$$A = \frac{\beta_p^m}{\beta_Q^m}, \quad B = a_p^m - a_Q^m \frac{\beta_p^m}{\beta_Q^m}. \qquad (74)$$

An equation of the form (70) for different series of compounds and different properties was found by Kireyev [13, 14] and then widely used by Karapet'yants [15,16] and thoroughly investigated by him for different properties. It was obtained by us for homologous groups of hydrocarbons as a result of laws of type (38) determined by us.

To the physico-chemical properties satisfying equation (38) and consequently also satisfying in pairs equation (70), belong the following:

    molecular volumes, molecular refraction, latent heat of vaporization, heat of crystallization*, the logarithm of the saturated vapour pressure, heats of combustion and formation from atoms and elements (simple substances) and (less accurately) the change in the thermodynamic potential during the formation of an alkane from simple substances.

Apparently, this equation is also satisfied by the average magnetic susceptibility of alkanes. In this way, each pair of the quantities enumerated above for each homologous group of alkanes can be connected by an equation of type (70).

Let us look at how accurately equation (70) is fulfilled for some physico-chemical quantities and homologous groups of alkanes, for which there are experimental data.

Graphs illustrating the accuracy of equation (70) are given in Figs. 21-23. From the diagrams it is evident that, according to the data available, equation (70) is satisfied sufficiently accurately for the investigated homologous groups of alkanes.

The importance of the laws expressed by equation (70) and

*For the heat of crystallization, this is shown only for normal alkanes [13].

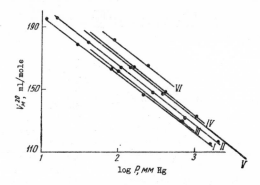

Fig. 21

The relation between V_M^{20} and log p of
a vapour at 60°C for different homologous groups of alkanes

I. *n*-alkanes; II. 2-methylalkanes; III. 3-methylalkanes;
IV. 2,2-dimethylalkanes; V. 2,(*n*-1)-dimethylalkanes;
VI. 2,2,(*n*-1)-trimethylalkanes

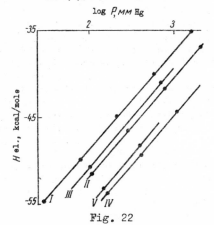

Fig. 22

Relation between the heat of formation of
gaseous alkanes at 25°C from elements
(simple substances) ΔH° (el.) and logarithm
of the vapour pressure at 60°C for differ-
ent groups of alkanes

I. *n*-alkanes; II. methylalkanes; III. 3-methylalkanes;
IV. 2,2-dimethylalkanes; V. 2,(*n*-1)-dimethylalkanes

illustrated by the diagrams consists of the fact that a knowledge of the coefficients A and B in this equation for a
given pair of physico-chemical quantities P and Q enables
the following problems to be solved:

1. Using the physico-chemical property Q of an alkane of
a given group, the property P of this alkane can be determined (and vice versa). This possibility can be of great
value, if the value of one of these properties (P or Q) is
easily determined experimentally or already known. In this
way, for example, it is possible to determine the heats of
combustion, of formation from the elements and other quantities which are hard to determine otherwise from the molecular
volume (density) or the refraction or the vapour pressure,
which are much more readily available and demand much less
difficult measurements.

2. The accuracy of new experimental values of P and Q
can be verified for newly synthesized alkanes of a given
homologous group. Values of the properties P and Q should
satisfy equation (70) or for a graphical check the corresponding point should lie on a straight line for a given homologous group.

3. Having measured the properties P and Q of a newly
synthesized alkane, one can check whether it belongs to that
homologous group to which it is assumed to belong, i.e. the
accuracy of the determination of its structure can be verified. Such a check can be done, e.g. graphically. The point
on the graph in the co-ordinates of P and Q should lie on
a straight line for alkanes of a given group. By using
several pairs of physico-chemical properties it seems that
this method can make it possible not only to verify but also
in certain cases to determine the structure of a new alkane.

4. The problem can be solved of the possibility of the
occurrence, within the limits of a given homologous group,
of an alkane with a given value of both physico-chemical
properties P and Q .

As was shown above, the possibilities enumerated in the
immediately preceding paragraphs 1-4 can occur; if the
coefficients A and B in equation (70) are known for a given
(m th) homologous group of alkanes. Coefficients A and B
in equation (70) can be calculated directly from the coeffi-
cients in equations (38) and (71), α_P^m, β_P^m, α_Q^m, β_Q^m , given for a
series of physico-chemical quantities in Table 12. It is

natural, however, that more exact values of the coefficients
A and B can be obtained not by this means but by calculating them directly from the comparison of equation (70) with
the experimental values of the properties P and Q of alkanes
of a given m th group, although the difference between the
methods of determination of the coefficients A and B can
often be substantial.

For convenience, values are given in Table 5 of the coefficients A and B for certain homologous groups of alkanes,
for which there are sufficiently reliable experimental data.
The values of these coefficients were calculated by the
method of least squares directly from experimental data with
the help of equation (70).

2. The Extension of the Method to the Case of Two Different Properties, Measured for Different Physical Conditions, of Two Different Homologous Groups of Alkanes

We have shown above that an equation of type (70) is correct for two different properties of those enumerated above,
for one and the same homologous group of alkanes. It is
easy to see that an equation of type (70) also holds for two
similar or different properties of those satisfying equation
(38) (i.e. of those enumerated in Section 1) referring to
different homologous groups of alkanes. The properties P
and Q being compared can refer to similar or different physical conditions (temperature, pressure, state of aggrega-
tion, etc.). Actually, if a certain property P of a homologous group of alkanes (e.g., the m th), measured during
specified physical conditions (T_1, p_1, ... etc.) satisfies an
equation of type (38) and another property of another homologous group of alkanes (e.g. k th), measured at other physical conditions (T_2, p_2 , ... etc.) also satisfies an equation of type (38), then evidently equation (70) is correct
for these properties since all the considerations used in its
deduction hold good. By considering the illustration of the
laws described above, the connexion can be seen in Fig. 24
between the heats of combustion of liquid alkanes and the
homologous group of 2,2-dimethylalkanes at 25°C, also the
molecular volumes of liquid n-alkanes and 2,2-dimethylal-
kanes at 20°C.

As can be seen from the diagram, between the quantities
mentioned, there actually exists a linear relation, which

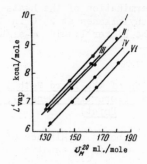

Fig. 23

The relation between $L°$ (vap.) in
an ideal gaseous state for the
temperature range 130-170°C and
the molecular volume V_M^{20} of alkanes, for different homologous
groups

I. n-alkanes; II. 2-methylalkanes; III. 3-methylalkanes;
IV. 2,2-dimethylalkanes; VI. 2,2,(n-1)-trimethylalkanes

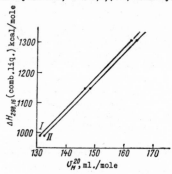

Fig. 24

The relation between heat of combustion
of liquid 2,2-dimethylalkanes $\Delta H_{298.16}$
(comb.liq.) and the molecular volume V_M^{20}

I. liquid n-alkanes; II. 2,2-dimethylalkanes

permits the simple determination of the heats of combustion of the higher 2,2-dimethylalkanes at 25°C in terms of the molecular volumes of the higher liquid n-alkanes at 20°C, which are known.

3. The Application of the Third Method to Other Physico-chemical Properties (Density, Boiling Point)

The density and boiling point of alkanes of a specified homologous group do not satisfy an equation of type (70). Therefore we cannot apply the third method of calculation directly to density or boiling point of the alkanes. Density can, of course, be determined from molecular volume, having determined the latter by one of the methods described above.

The problem of the connexion between density or any function of density of alkanes of a given homologous group and other physico-chemical properties of alkanes of the same or different homologous groups can be decided in the following way. The equation

$$d_n^m = A^m + \frac{B^m}{n_0^m + n} \tag{58}$$

determines the variation of the density d_n^m of the alkane C_nH_{2n+2} of a homologous group with n. From this equation it follows that a function of density will vary linearly with respect to n

$$\frac{1}{d_n^m - A^m} = \frac{n_0^m}{B^m} + \frac{1}{B^m}n = $$
$$= \alpha_d^m + \beta_d^m n. \tag{75}$$

The illustration of this is given in Fig. 25.

In connexion with the quantities $\frac{1}{d_n^m - A^m}$, everything written above with respect to the property P , satisfying equation (38), holds good. Thus, for example, the quantity $(d_n^m - A^m)^{-1}$ in a given m th group of alkanes will be connected linearly with other physico-chemical properties P for alkanes of that m th group, which satisfy equation (38):

$$\frac{1}{d_n^m - A^m} = AP_n^m + B, \tag{76}$$

where P_n^m can be the molecular volume, refraction, logarithm of the vapour pressure, heat of formation from atoms or elements, heat of combustion, etc. (Fig. 26). In connexion with the quantity $(d_n^m - A^m)^{-1}$, everything written in Section 2 is correct.

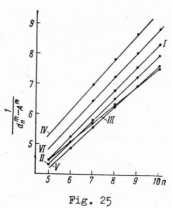

Fig. 25

The relation between the quantity $\dfrac{1}{d_n^m - A^m}$ and the number of carbon atoms for different groups of alkanes

I. n-alkanes; II. 2-methylalkanes; III. 3-methylalkanes; IV. 3-ethylalkanes; V. 2,2-dimethylalkanes; VI. 2,3-dimethylalkanes; (The values of density d_4^{20} used are from Table 13)

In particular, the equation

$$\frac{1}{d_n^m - A^m} = AP_n^k + B. \tag{77}$$

will be correct.

In other words, the magnitude $(d_n^m - A^m)^{-1}$ for alkanes of the mth homologous group is connected linearly with any physico-chemical characteristic P_n^k of alkanes of the kth homologous group, satisfying equation (38), which is seen in Fig. 26. Boiling point, as we saw above, is quite accurately described by a function of n, similarly to density:

$$t_{n,\text{boil}}^m = t_0^m + \frac{C^m}{n_0^m + n}. \tag{67}$$

From this formula it follows that $(t^m_{n.boil} - t^m_0)^{-1}$ varies linearly with n:

$$\frac{1}{t^m_{n,boil} - t^m_0} = \frac{n^m_0}{C^m} + \frac{1}{C^m}n = a^m_t + \beta^m_t n. \qquad (78)$$

This rule is illustrated in Fig. 27.

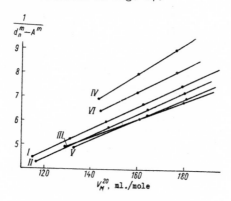

Fig. 26

The relation between the quantity

$\frac{1}{d^m_n - A^m} \cdot$ and the molecular volume

of the different homologous groups
of alkanes

I. n-alkanes; II. 2-dimethylalkanes; III. 3-methylalkanes;
IV. 3-ethylalkanes; V. 2,2-dimethylalkanes; VI. 2,3-di-
methylalkanes; (The values of d^{20}_4 and V^{20}_M are used from
Table 13)

Therefore, in connexion with the function $(t^m_{n,boil} - t^m_0)^{-1}$, everything written above referring to the physico-chemical quantities satisfying equation (38) will be correct. In other words, for this function, the equation

$$\frac{1}{t^m_{n,boil} - t^m_0} = AP^m_n + B, \qquad (79)$$

will be correct, where P^m_n is one of the physico-chemical properties, enumerated above, of the same mth group, which satisfy equation (38) (Fig. 28).

It is evident that for two homologous groups of alkanes (mth and kth) the equation

$$\frac{1}{t^m_{n\cdot\text{boil}}-t^m_0} = AP^k_n + B. \qquad (80)$$

is also correct.

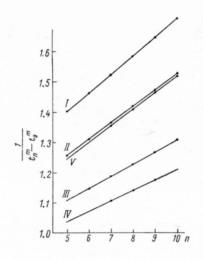

Fig. 27

The relation between the quantity
$\frac{1}{t^m_n-t^m_0}$ and the number of carbon
atoms   of the homologous groups
of alkanes
I. n-alkanes;   II. 2-methylalkanes;   III. 3-methylalkanes;
IV. 2,2-dimethylalkanes;   V. 2,3-dimethylalkanes.   The
values of the boiling points refer to a normal pressure
of 760 mm mercury

It should be emphasized that the constants A and B, for each pair of specified physico-chemical quantities and for each two compared homologous groups, will of course have different values.

In this way the third method of calculation cannot be applied directly to density or boiling point but the functions described above of these quantities are obtained by this method. The application of the third method to the function $(d_n^m - A^m)^{-1}$ and $(t_{n,\,boil}^m - t_0^m)^{-1}$ is not very suitable in practice, since equations (76) and (78) contain, in fact, three constants A^m (or t_0^m), A and B. The determination of these constants is no easier than the determination of the three constants in equations (58) or (67) and require no less data.

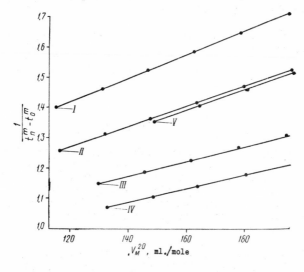

Fig. 28

The relation between the quantity $\dfrac{1}{t_{n,\,boil}^m - t_0^m}$ and the molecular volume of homologous groups of alkanes

I. n-alkanes; II. 2-methylalkanes; III. 3-methylalkanes;
IV. 2,2-dimethylalkanes; V. 2,(n-1)-dimethylalkanes

In particular cases (for large values of n) equations (58) and (67) can be written in the form

$$d_n^m = A^m + \frac{B^m}{n}, \qquad (81)$$

$$t_n^m = t_0^m + \frac{C^m}{n}. \qquad (82)$$

From equations (81) and (82) it follows that

$$d_n^{m\cdot} = At_{n,\text{boil}}^m + B, \tag{83}$$

that is, there exists a linear variation of density with the boiling point of alkanes of one homologous group. This equation can be used for the calculation of one of the physico-chemical characteristics by using another for higher alkanes, as was described earlier.

From equations (81) and (82) for different homologous groups it follows also that

$$d_n^m = Ad_n^k + B \tag{84}$$

and

$$d_n^m = At_{n,\text{boil}}^k + B, \tag{85}$$

where the quantities on the right and left sides of the equations refer to different homologous groups. These variations, approximately correct for large n, that is for higher alkanes, can arouse a certain interest for the calculation of densities and boiling points of higher alkanes of one group using these quantities for another homologous group, as described earlier.

The laws, established above, connecting different physico-chemical properties of different homologous groups of alkanes enable the determination in a quite simple way, of a large collection of physico-chemical properties of higher alkanes of a series of homologous groups.

Everything described above in connexion with the possibilities of using equation (70) in the case when the properties P and Q refer to one homologous group, holds good for its wider application, when the properties P and Q refer to different homologous groups and different physical conditions

CHAPTER IV

A COMPARISON OF THE THREE METHODS OF
CALCULATION

To compare the three methods of calculation, outlined
above, it is necessary to consider them from two aspects:

1) with respect to the accuracy attainable by each method
and the conditions which guarantee the attainment of a sufficiently high accuracy of calculation;

2) with respect to the quantity of the initial experimental data for lower alkanes necessary for the calculation of
the physico-chemical characteristics of the higher alkanes
and the extent of the range of alkanes of different structure, the physico-chemical properties of which can be calculated by each method.

1. A Comparison of the Accuracy of the Three
Methods of Calculation

During the comparison of the three methods of calculation
it should be remembered that the possible inaccuracies of
these methods arise from two essentially different sources.

The first source is the degree of conformity of the equations in these methods to the actual relationships of the
properties of the alkanes; that is the accuracy of the
values obtainable by each of the three methods depends on
how objectively correct is the form of the equations of each
of these methods. As will be shown below the equations of
the three methods, in the forms in which they were used above,
are not identical in the general sense.

The second source is the accuracy with which the constants
used in the corresponding equations can be determined.

65

Actually, each of the three methods includes such constant as can be determined from known experimental data for the lower alkanes. In the first method such constants are the nine constants P_{ij}; in the second method the constants α^m and β^m for each of the homologous groups of alkanes; in th third method the coefficients A and B in the linear depend ency of the two properties P and Q.

All these constants are determined from the experimentally measured properties of the lower alkanes, which are always subject to a certain amount of experimental error, which results in the calculated values of the constants P_{ij}, α^m, β^m, A and B in each of these methods also not being completely accurate, i.e. they are not the optimum values. It is natur that the accuracy of the calculations by each of the methods depends on the accuracy of the corresponding constants. The accuracy of the values of the constants in each of the metho depends on the accuracy of those experimental data for lower alkanes, from which these constants were obtained.

Let us assume, firstly, that the accuracy of the experimen tal data for the lower alkanes, used for determining the con stants of the three methods, is so high that we can for practical purposes consider the experimental values for the lower alkanes used to be true. Then the whole error of cal culation in each method is defined only by the degree of accuracy of the formulae of the particular method, that is the extent of the agreement of the formulae of each method to the actual quantitative relationships of the properties of the alkanes.

It is easily seen that under these conditions the most exact values will be given by the method of comparative cal culation, i.e. the third method. Actually, this method is the direct mathematical result of the equations of the first two methods. Therefore the values of the properties, obtain by this method, cannot be less exact than the values obtaine by the first two methods, providing that the constants A an B are obtained from accurate experimental values of the pro perties of lower alkanes and that for one of the compared properties, which leads to the determination of the other, accurate values are known for higher alkanes of the corres ponding homologous group. However, the third (comparative) method also has special features that can result in its accuracy being not only, not lower, but even somewhat higher than that of the other two methods, especially for alkanes with a very large value for n. Indeed, from the equations

of the first and second methods, it follows that such proper-
ties as V_M, R_M, ΔH (at.), ΔH (el.), ΔH (comb.), L (vap.), L (cryst.)
in each homologous group of alkanes, varies strictly linearly
with respect to n. The equations of the third method are
strictly correct when such linear variations occur, but as
was shown by Karapet'yants [15,16], they are also correct in
a more general case, that is if, in the two homologous groups,
the properties P and Q do not vary linearly with n but are
expressed in the forms

$$P = a_1 + b_1 f(n),$$
$$Q = a_2 + b_2 f(n), \tag{86}$$

where a_1 and a_2, b_1 and b_2 are constants, but $f(n)$ for both
properties is one and the same function of n *

If the variation of the properties P and Q with respect
to n is, in fact, not strictly linear, especially for a considerable range of the values of n, but can perhaps be expressed to a sufficiently accurate approximation in the form
(86), then the third method remains valid to the degree of
accuracy applying to the relationships (86), when the first
and second methods are inaccurate and lead to errors, measured
by the degree of deviation of equations (37) from a linear
function of n.

It is easily seen that if the properties P and Q vary
non-linearly with n, but the deviations from linearity are
small, then they can always be expressed with greater accuracy
by functions of type (86) than by linear equations with respect to n, and therefore the third method of calculation
will always give more accurate values than the first two.

In this way, providing that accurate values of the properties of the lower alkanes are used for the determination of
the constants of each method (P_{ij}, α and β, A and B) and
that accurate values for one of the properties (P or Q)
in one homologous group of alkanes are known, the values of
the other property (Q or P) calculated by the third method
will be either as accurate as or more accurate than those
calculated by the first two methods.

---

*In fact, we obtain from (86) $\dfrac{P-a_1}{Q-a_2} = \dfrac{b_1}{b_2}$, or

$$P = \frac{b_1}{b_2} Q + a_1 - \frac{b_1}{b} a_2 = AQ + B.$$

If, under the conditions set out above the first and second methods of calculation are compared, then it seems that the second method is more accurate than the first. Indeed the formulae of the second method are always accurate, if the formulae of the first method are accurate, as the former can be derived from the latter as was shown above. However, the formulae of the second method in that form, where α^m and β^m, generally speaking, are different for each homologous group of alkanes and are determined for each homologous group independently, are much more general than the formulae of the first method and cannot be derived from the formulae of the first method. Actually, the values of β for different homologous groups, if they are determined from equations of the first method, are equal for all groups, but the values of α for different groups are not independent, but are expressed by means of the constants P_{ij} (or P_{12}, P_{22} and G_{ij}).

At the same time, if the second method is applied in that form, where α^m and β^m for each homologous group are determined independently from various experimental data for the lower alkanes, such restrictions are not imposed on the constants α^m and β^m of the different groups. Under these conditions it is possible to convey more accurately the variation of the appropriate property with respect to n than it is possible to do by using the equations of the first method, where α^m and β^m in the equations for different homologous groups are linked with rather rigid conditions described above. In this way, when accurate data are available on the properties of the lower alkanes, from which constants in the equations of the first and second methods are determined, the latter method for the calculation of the properties of the higher alkanes gives greater or at least as good accuracy as the first method.

Let us look now at the question of the influence of the errors in the experimental values of the properties of the lower alkanes, used for the calculation of the constants P_{ij} α and β, A and B of the three methods, on the accuracy of the values of the properties of the higher alkanes, calculated by means of these methods.

Whilst considering this question, we have to assume, in contrast to the preceding, that the equations of all three methods are on the whole completely accurate, that is they accurately reflect the relationships of the corresponding physico-chemical properties of alkanes and all the errors in the calculation of the properties of the higher alkanes arise as a result of the inaccuracy of the constants P_{ij}, α and β, A and B, obtained from inaccurate values of the properties of the lower alkanes, and in the third method also from the inaccuracy of the values of one of the properties (for example Q) of higher alkanes of one of the homologous groups, used for the comparative method of calculation (that is for the determination of the properties of the higher alkanes).

Under these stipulated conditions - the same principal accuracy of the form of the equations for all methods* - the first and second methods are obtained mathematically by means of identities, since for each homologous group of alkanes, equations of the first method agree exactly with equations of the second method (Chapter II, section 1).

The differences between the first and second methods arise from the fact that the constants α^m and β^m of the second method are determined from values of the properties of the lower alkanes of only one homologous group, whilst the constants of the first method are determined from the values of the properties of lower alkanes not included in such homologous groups. In this way, under these conditions, the constants of the first method should be more exact since in their determination a larger number of experimental values of the properties of the lower alkanes is used and the errors in these properties**, in accordance with statistical laws, have less effect on the accuracy of the constants P_{ij}, than α and β.

Consequently, the first method under the stipulated conditions is more exact and in any case not less exact than the second. In the third method of calculation, the values of the property P, obtained for higher alkanes depend not only on the accuracy of the values of the property P for lower alkanes, which are used for the determination of the constants A and B, but also on the accuracy of the values of the property Q for the lower alkanes, which are also necessary for the calculation of the constants A and B. Besides this, for the calculation of the property P for higher alkanes for known A and B it is necessary to know the values of the property Q for the corresponding higher alkanes of one of

---

*This corresponds to the case when β is the same for all homologous groups of alkanes but α is expressed by P_{12}, P_{22}, G_{ij} in accordance with equation (37).

**It is assumed that they are isolated and not of a systematic character.

F

the homologous groups. The errors in the calculated values
of the property P of the higher alkanes will, consequently,
arise not only as a result of the inaccuracy of the values
of the properties P and Q of the lower alkanes, but also
from the inaccuracy of the values of the property Q of higher
alkanes of that homologous group, for which the calculation
of the property P is being conducted. Evidently under the
stipulated conditions, the third method of calculation contains more sources of error than the first two, and values
obtained by this method will be less exact than by the first
two methods.

Thus, the errors in the values of the property P for lower
alkanes, from which the constants of the different methods
are obtained (or the errors in the values of the property Q
both for lower and higher alkanes of the homologous group,
for which the calculation is conducted in the case of the
third method) cause a severe reduction in the accuracy of the
third method, a lesser reduction for the second method and an
even lesser reduction for the first method.

2. The Initial Data on the Properties of Alkanes Necessary for the Calculation of the Properties of Higher Alkanes for each of the Three Methods of Calculation, and the Total Range of Alkanes for which the Calculation of Properties is Possible

Data on the properties of alkanes are limited and are more
or less complete only for alkanes from C_1 to C_8. There are
little data on the properties of the C_9 and C_{10} alkanes, and
for alkanes with a larger number of carbon atoms there are
only isolated data. It is therefore natural that the quantity
of initial data, necessary for the calculation of the properties of the higher alkanes by each of the three methods, is
in practice very important and to a large extent determines
the practical possibility of achieving the calculation of the
properties of this or that higher alkane by each of the three
methods.

Let us look at this question with respect to each of the
three methods: the first method of calculation, within the
limits of the assumptions made in the derivation of the fundamental equation (4) of this method, permits chiefly the
evaluation of the properties of any higher alkanes obeying
equation (4) (Section 1, introduction), if the nine constants

P_{ij}, occurring in equation (4) are known. For the determination of these constants, it is necessary to possess experimental data on the properties of those lower alkanes, in which the C—C bonds of all nine forms (sub-types) would be encountered. All nine forms of these bonds occur in the $C_3 - C_8$ alkanes, but the $C_4 - C_4$ bond is encountered in the $C_3 - C_8$ alkanes only once, i.e. in 2,2,3,3-tetramethylbutane.

To determine the value of the constant P_{44} sufficiently reliably, it is evidently necessary to know the properties of some (two or three) higher alkanes containing the $C_4 - C_4$ bond, besides the C_3-C_8 alkanes. Then all the constants P_{ij} in the equation of the first method can be verified many times and their knowledge permits chiefly (not taking into account the question of accuracy discussed above) the calculation of the properties for any higher alkanes that satisfy equation (4).

Generally speaking, for the determination of the nine constants P_{ij} it is obligatory to know the property P of all the $C_3 - C_8$ alkanes. For their determination it is sufficient to know the properties of a minimum of nine alkanes, which must, however, contain C — C bonds of all nine forms. Among these nine alkanes there cannot be two or more belonging to one homologous group. Such is the minimum range of the initial data necessary for the calculation by the first method of the corresponding properties of any higher alkane. With respect to the second and third methods of calculation it should be mentioned, above all, that the properties of certain alkanes, not falling into one homologous group*, in general cannot be calculated by these methods. To these alkanes, for example, belong the lower alkanes 2,2-dimethylpropane; 2,3-dimethylbutane; 2,2,3-trimethylbutane; 2,2,3, 3-tetramethylbutane and many higher alkanes, the number of which increases with increase in n .

Whilst using the second method of calculation, a linear formula with respect to n , with two constants α and β , is developed for homologous groups. For the calculation of the properties of higher alkanes by this method, it is necessary to know the corresponding property of a minimum of two lower alkanes of the same homologous group. More reliable values of α and β , and simultaneously, a check on the linear dependency on n , can be obtained, if the corresponding

---

*Or, in other words, which are isolated members existing in a characteristic homologous group.

property is known for three or four alkanes of a given homologous group.

Since the number of homologous groups of alkanes grows with
increase of n and many higher alkanes belong to homologous
groups, in which n would be greater than or equal to 10, the
number of data for such alkanes being insufficient makes it
evident that, in relation to the range of its possible application, the second method is at present restricted in practice
to homologous groups, starting with the $C_3 - C_8$ alkanes. The
greater n becomes, the less isomers of higher alkanes are
present in these homologous groups.

The third method demands, for the calculation of the property P of higher alkanes of a given homologous group, the
same data as the second requires and also values of the property Q of the lower (for determining A and B) and of the
higher (for calculating the property P) alkanes of that
homologous group for which the calculation is being carried
out.

It is clear from what has been said that, in relation to
the necessary initial data and the width of the range of the
higher alkanes for which the calculation of properties is
possible, the first method possesses the greater possibilities. It permits the calculation of properties of any higher
alkanes and demands essentially a minimum knowledge of the
properties of nine lower alkanes.

We cannot apply the second method generally to all higher
alkanes; it demands a knowledge of the properties of not
less than two alkanes of a given group; these two alkanes
can be higher alkanes and permit the calculation from these
data only of properties of the alkanes of the same group. Thus,
for the calculation of the properties of higher alkanes with
increase in n , more and more initial data are necessary,
since the number of homologous groups increases with increase
in n . With increase in n , groups appear which start only
with large n ; this demands a knowledge of the properties
of a minimum of two higher alkanes for the determination of
the constants α and β .

The third method also demands a knowledge not only of the
property P to be calculated, but also of the property Q
which is to be compared with it, since the property Q should
be known not only for two lower alkanes, so that A and B
can be determined, but also for all those higher alkanes of

one homologous group, to make possible the calculation of the property *P* by the comparison method in the same or another homologous group.

In this way, with regard to the initial data required, the first method is comparatively more economical than the second, and the second more than the third. With regard to the number and structure of the alkanes for which the properties can be calculated, the first method gives the greatest possibilities, but the second and third methods possess possibilities which are restricted both in principle and in practice.

3. Conclusion

As has been said above, the three described methods of calculating physico-chemical properties of alkanes possess their own characteristics. They differ with respect to accuracy, the range of initial data necessary, and the range of alkanes for which the calculation of properties is possible. It is evident that these methods supplement one another, and when possible should be used jointly for mutual checking purposes.

It follows from the remarks above that today for mass calculation of the physico-chemical properties of higher alkanes, in practice only the first method can be used, but the second and third methods can serve to verify and define more precisely the properties only of higher alkanes of isolated homologous groups.

TABLES

TABLE 1

Forms (sub-types) of the **C—H** and **C—C** bonds in alkanes and symbols of the number of bonds of different sub-types and partial quantities p_i or p_{ij}, corresponding to the bonds of different sub-types[*]

Form (sub-type) of bond	Bond	No. of bonds in a molecule	physico-chemical value relating to the bond	Form (sub-type) of bond	Bond	No. of bonds in a molecule	physico-chemical value relating to the bond
Bonds $>$C—H				3. H—C—C—C (H, H / C, H)	C_1—C_3	n_{13}	p_{13}
1. H—C—H (H, H / H)	C_0—H	n_0	p_0	4. H—C—C—C (H, H / C, C)	C_1—C_4	n_{14}	p_{14}
2. H—C—H (H, C / H)	C_1—H	n_1	p_1	5. H—C—C—H (C, C / H, H)	C_2—C_2	n_{22}	p_{22}
3. C—C—H (H, C / C)	C_2—H	n_2	p_2	6. H—C—C—C (C, C / H, H)	C_2—C_3	n_{23}	p_{23}
4. C—C—H (C, C / C)	C_3—H	n_3	p_3	7. H—C—C—C (C, C / H, C)	C_2—C_4	n_{24}	p_{24}
Bonds $>$C—C$<$				8. C—C—C—C (C, C / H, H)	C_3—C_3	n_{33}	p_{33}
1. H—C—C—H (H, H / H, H)	C_1—C_1	n_{11}	p_{11}	9. C—C—C—C (C, C / H, C)	C_3—C_4	n_{34}	p_{34}
2. H—C—C—C (H, H / H, H)	C_1—C_2	n_{12}	p_{12}	10. C—C—C—C (C, C / C, C)	C_4—C_4	n_{44}	p_{44}

[*] C_0, C_1, C_2, C_3, C_4 indicate, respectively, the C atom in methane, the primary, secondary, tertiary and quaternary C atoms.

TABLE 2

The values of V_{ij}^{20} and V_{ij}^{25} for the calculation of the molecular volumes of the alkanes, V_M^{20} and V_M^{25}

V_{ij}	V_{ij} in ml./mole at temperature	
	20° C	25° C
V_{12}	41.472	41.91
V_{13}	33.979	34.25
V_{14}	29.965	30.13
V_{22}	16.002	16.01
V_{23}	6.479	6.43
V_{24}	1.003	0.67
V_{33}	$-$ 5.356	$-$ 5.61
V_{34}	$-$12.624	$-$12.92
V_{44}	$-$22.596	$-$22.75

TABLE 3

The quantities R_{ij}^{20} and R_{ij}^{25} for the calculation of the molecular refractions of the alkanes, R_M^{20} and R_M^{25}

R_{ij}	R_{ij} in ml./mole for temperatures	
	20° C	25° C
R_{12}	7.986	7.996
R_{13}	6.934	6.944
R_{14}	6.388	6.396
R_{22}	4.645	4.637
R_{23}	3.446	3.442
R_{24}	2.793	2.785
R_{33}	2.091	2.092
R_{34}	1.352	1.348
R_{44}	0.506	0.510

TABLE 4

Values of L_{ij} and B_{ij} for different temperature ranges

L_{ij} and B_{ij}	L_{ij} and B_{ij} in cal/mole for temperature ranges				
	40—80° C	70—110° C	90—130° C	110—150° C	130—170° C
L_{12}	2154.8	2154.8	2154.8	2154.8	2154.8
L_{13}	1656.2	1631.9	1623.2	1620.5	1615.9
L_{14}	1331.3	1340.0	1326.3	1313.9	1309.8
L_{22}	1040.4	964.4	924.6	888.5	857.4
L_{23}	517.4	456.1	409.9	365.1	320.3
L_{24}	297.4	197.2	156.5	116.2	80.5
L_{33}	240.2	140.5	80.1	17.4	—49.9
L_{34}	105.7	—38.0	—84.6	—141.8	—190.8
B_{12}	7.8424	7.8424	7.8424	7.8424	7.8390
B_{13}	5.3547	5.3160	5.3080	5.3008	5.2914
B_{14}	4.0250	4.0305	4.0118	3.9946	3.9916
B_{22}	0.6078	0.5002	0.4459	0.4007	0.3632
B_{23}	—1.9495	—2.0301	—2.0957	—2.1475	—2.1989
B_{24}	—3.2270	—3.3548	—3.4135	—3.4612	—3.5036
B_{33}	—4.3474	—4.4819	—4.5668	—4.6424	—4.6875
B_{34}	—5.5097	—5.7720	—5.8492	—5.9113	—5.9735

TABLE 5

Values of λ_{ij} for different temperature ranges

λ_{ij}	λ_{ij} in cal/mole for temperature ranges				
	40—80° C	70—110° C	90—130° C	110—150° C	130—170° C
λ_{12}	471.0	471.0	470.6	471.0	471.0
λ_{22}	227.4	210.8	202.1	194.2	187.4
λ_{13}	362.0	356.7	354.8	354.2	353.2
λ_{23}	113.1	99.7	89.6	79.8	70.0
λ_{14}	291.0	292.9	289.2	287.2	286.3
λ_{24}	65.0	43.1	34.2	25.4	47.6
λ_{33}	52.5	30.7	17.5	3.8	—10.9
λ_{34}	23.1	—8.3	—18.5	—31.0	—41.7
λ_{44}	—	—	—	—	—

TABLE 6

Values of the constants b_{ij} for alkanes

b_{ij}	b_{ij} for temperature ranges				
	40—80° C	70—110° C	90—130° C	110—150° C	130—170° C
b_{12}	3.4053	3.4053	3.4053	3.4053	3.4038
b_{22}	0.2639	0.2172	0.1936	0.1740	0.1577
b_{13}	2.3251	2.3083	2.3048	2.3017	2.2976
b_{23}	—0.8465	—0.8815	—0.9100	—0.9325	—0.9548
b_{14}	1.7477	1.7501	1.7420	1.7345	1.7332
b_{24}	—1.4012	—1.4567	—1.4822	—1.5029	—1.5213
b_{33}	—1.8877	—1.9461	—1.9830	—2.0158	—2.0354
b_{34}	—2.3924	—2.5063	—2.5398	—2.5668	—2.5938

TABLE 7

Values of π_{ij} for the calculation of the logarithms of the vapour pressure of alkanes

π_{ij}	π_{ij} for temperature				
	60° C	90° C	110° C	130° C	150° C
π_{12}	1.9917	2.1085	2.1762	2.2372	2.2909
π_{13}	1.2387	1.3262	1.3789	1.4232	1.4630
π_{14}	0.8744	0.9437	0.9855	1.0222	1.0567
π_{22}	—0.4185	—0.3632	—0.3338	—0.3076	—0.2851
π_{23}	—1.1859	—1.1560	—1.1438	—1.1304	—1.1202
π_{24}	—1.5963	—1.5752	—1.5714	—1.5659	—1.5629
π_{33}	—2.0453	—2.0306	—2.0287	—2.0252	—2.0096
π_{34}	—2.4617	—2.4834	—2.4916	—2.4899	—2.4953

TABLE 8

Values of Π_{ij} for the calculation of the vapour pressure of alkanes

Π_{ij}	Π_{ij} for temperature				
	60° C	90° C	110° C	130°C	150° C
Π_{12}	98.11	128.4	150.0	172.7	195.4
Π_{13}	17.33	21.19	23.93	26.50	29.04
Π_{14}	7.49	8.78	9.67	10.52	11.4
Π_{22}	0.38	0.43	0.46	0.49	0.52
Π_{23}	0.065	0.070	0.072	0.074	0.076
Π_{24}	0.025	0.027	0.027	0.027	0.027
Π_{33}	0.0090	0.0093	0.0094	0.0094	0.0098
Π_{34}	0.00035	0.00033	0.00032	0.00032	0.00032

TABLE 9

Values of H_{ij}° (at.), H_{ij}° (el.), H_{ij}° (comb.) for gaseous
and liquid alkanes at 298.16°K in kcal/mole

H_{ij}	H_{ij} (at.gas)	H_{ij}(el.,gas)	H_{ij}(comb.,gas)	H_{ij} (comb.,liq.)
H_{12}	—477.27	—12.54	—265.17	—263.24
H_{13}	—412.31	—10.79	—228.48	—226.99
H_{14}	—379.94	—10.03	—210.01	—208.68
H_{22}	—280.06	— 4.96	—157.41	—156.23
H_{23}	—214.46	— 2.58	—121.35	—120.45
H_{24}	—181.63	— 1.35	— 103.35	—102.70
H_{33}	—147.69	+ 0.98	— 86.45	— 85.55
H_{34}	—113.92	+ 3.14	— 69.40	— 68.90
H_{44}	— 79.27	+ 6.19	— 53.22	— (—53.77) *

TABLE 10

The values of Z_{ij} for the calculation of ΔZ°
for the formation of the gaseous alkanes
from simple substances (graphite and
molecular hydrogen) at various
temperatures

Z_{ij}	Z_{ij} in kcal/mole at temperatures		
	298.16° K	500° K	700° K
Z_{12}	—3.13	3.77	11.10
Z_{13}	—1.83	4.59	11.33
Z_{14}	—1.09	5.27	11.86
Z_{22}	2.03	6.89	11.90
Z_{23}	3.81	8.10	12.47
Z_{24}	4.86	8.91	13.03
Z_{33}	6.55	10.32	14.05
Z_{34}	8.28	11.57	14.88
Z_{44}	11.77	15.32	18.79

*The value of H_{44} (comb., liq.) is not very exact since it was obtained from a value
of ΔH°(comb.) for only one hydrocarbon.
The values of H_{ij} (at., gas) were calculated by reckoning that the most probable
value today of the heat of sublimation of graphite (at T = 298.16 °K) is given by

$$\Delta H^\circ_{C_\beta 298.16} = 170.917 \text{ kcal/gm.at.}$$

This explains the differences between the values of H_{ij} (at., gas), given in Table
9 and the values given in [31].

TABLE 10 (contd.)

Values of z_{ij} for the calculation of the equilibrium constants K_p according to the formulae (17) and (18)

ζ_{ij}	ζ_{ij} at temperatures		
	298,16° K	500° K	700° K
ς_{12}	$1.972 \cdot 10^2$	$2.249 \cdot 10^{-2}$	$3.420 \cdot 10^{-4}$
ς_{13}	$2.198 \cdot 10^1$	$9.863 \cdot 10^{-3}$	$2.897 \cdot 10^{-4}$
ς_{14}	$6.296 \cdot 10^0$	$5.117 \cdot 10^{-3}$	$1.972 \cdot 10^{-4}$
ζ_{22}	$3.251 \cdot 10^{-2}$	$9.727 \cdot 10^{-4}$	$1.923 \cdot 10^{-4}$
ς_{23}	$1.384 \cdot 10^{-3}$	$2.871 \cdot 10^{-4}$	$1.276 \cdot 10^{-4}$
ζ_{24}	$2.735 \cdot 10^{-4}$	$1.274 \cdot 10^{-4}$	$8.933 \cdot 10^{-5}$
ς_{33}	$1.581 \cdot 10^{-5}$	$3.083 \cdot 10^{-5}$	$4.198 \cdot 10^{-5}$
ς_{34}	$8.511 \cdot 10^{-7}$	$8.730 \cdot 10^{-6}$	$2.249 \cdot 10^{-5}$
ς_{44}	$2.594 \cdot 10^{-9}$	$2.000 \cdot 10^{-7}$	$1.355 \cdot 10^{-6}$

TABLE 11

Branched alkanes in homologous groups with approximately constant value of Δ (examples of groups with approximately constant values of Δ)

No.of group	Homologous group	Expression for Δ in terms of G_{ij}
1	n–alkanes	0
2	2-methylalkanes (beginning with C_5H_{12})	
3	3-methylalkanes (beginning with C_6H_{14})	$2G_{13} + G_{23}$
	4-methylalkanes (beginning with C_8H_{18})	$G_{13} + 2G_{23}$
4	3-ethylalkanes (beginning with C_7H_{16})	
	4-ethylalkanes (beginning with C_9H_{20})	$2G_{23}$
5	2,2-dimethylalkanes (beginning with C_6H_{14})	$3G_{14} + G_{34}$
6	2,3-dimethylalkanes (beginning with C_7H_{16})	$3G_{13} + G_{23} + G_{33}$
7	2,4-dimethylalkanes (beginning with C_8H_{18})	
	2,5-dimethylalkanes (beginning with C_9H_{20})	$3G_{13} + 3G_{23}$
8	3,3-dimethylalkanes (beginning with C_7H_{16})	$2G_{14} + 2G_{24}$
9	3,4-dimethylalkanes (beginning with C_8H_{18})	
	2-methyl-3-ethylalkanes (beginning with C_8H_{18})	$2G_{13} + 2G_{23} + G_{33}$
10	2,3,3-trimethylalkanes (beginning with C_8H_{18})	$2G_{13} + 2G_{14} + G_{24} + G_{34}$
11	2,4-dimethylpentane	
	2,5-dimethylhexane	$4G_{13} + 2G_{23}$
	2,6-dimethylheptane	
12	2,2,4-trimethylpentane	
	2,2,5-trimethylhexane	$2G_{13} + G_{23} + 3G_{14} + G_{24}$
	2,2,6-trimethylheptane	

TABLE 12

Values of α^m and β^m for different physico-chemical properties of some homologous groups of alkanes

Homologous groups	V_M^{20}, ml./mole		$\Delta H°$ (el.) kcal/mole		$L°$ (vap.) cal/mole $t=130°$ $-170°$ C		log p in mm mercury at 60°C		d_4^{20}, g/ml			$t_{boil}(p=760$ mm mercury)		
	α_v	β_v	α_H	β_H	α_L	α_L	α_p	β_p	A	B	n_o	t_o, °C	—C	n_o
n-alkanes	34.044	16.108	−10.25	−4.95	1750	857	5.322	−0.428	0.84957	−1.28753	0.7647	782.18	16402	17.98
2-methylalkanes	37.020	15.838	−12.58	−4.86	1843	811	5.401	−0.421	0.85262	−1.37954	0.920	822.93	18724	18.55
3-methylalkanes	33.313	16.069	−11.57	−4.91	2041	784	5.307	−0.412	0.86817	−1.59149	1.800	934.97	25591	23.36
3-ethylalkanes	29.760	16.270	−9.92	−5.06	—	—	5.084	−0.383	0.84126	−1.28487	1.280	2683.02	265104	95.38
2,2-dimethylalkanes	37.401	15.888	−16.36	−4.68	1516	789	5.452	−0.406	0.8548	−1.4224	0.9172	983.95	28701	24.72
2,3-dimethylalkanes	30.63	16.22	−23.05	−3.51	1805	791	5.184	−0.389	0.8503	−1.2410	1.000	1246.52	50390	36.56
2,4-dimethylalkanes	31.90	16.38	—	—	—	—	—	—	0.7781	−0.3085	−4.0305	—	—	—
3,3-dimethylalkanes	32.84	15.98	−17.09	−4.44	1604	792	5.201	−0.383	1.0401	−6.8839	−12.770	1603.43	87344	50.56
3,4-dimethylalkanes	31.41	15.95	—	—	—	—	—	—	0.5830	−6.6562	−20.160	—	—	—
2,(n-1)-dimethylalkanes	37.00	15.98	−13.93	−4.91	581	921	5.569	−0.425	0.8693	−1.6613	1.450	818.62	18380	17.90
2,2,(n-1)-trimethylalkanes	34.99	15.98	—	—	785	840	6.879	−0.562	0.8327	−1.1545	0.200	—	—	—
2,2,3,3-tetramethylalkanes (beginning with C_8H_{20})	20.00	16.61	—	—	—	—	—	—	—	—	—	—	—	—

TABLE 13

Experimental and calculated* values, by the first method, of the molecular volumes $V_M{}^{20}$ and densities d_4^{20} of alkanes

Hydrocarbon	Purity in mol. %	$V_M{}^{20}$, ml./mole		d_4^{20}, g/ml.	
		exp. from [49, 50]	Calculated from eq. (4a)	exp. from [49, 50]	Calculated from eq. (19)
Propane	—	—	82.94	—	0.5316
n-Butane	—	—	98.95	—	0.5874
2-Methylpropane	—	—	101.94	—	0.5701
n-Pentane	99.87	115.20	114.95	0.62630	0.6276
2-Methylbutane	—	116.43	115.91	0.61963	0.6224
2,2-Dimethylpropane	—	—	119.86	—	0.6019
n-Hexane	99.91	130.95	130.69	0.65937	0.6594
2-Methylpentane	99.89	131.93	131.91	0.65315	0.6533
3- "	—	129.72	129.88	0.66431	0.6635
2,2-Dimethylbutane	99.94	132.74	132.34	0.64916	0.6511
2,3- "	99.90	130.24	130.58	0.66164	0.6599
n-Heptane	99.98	146.56	146.95	0.68366	0.6819
2-Methylhexane	99.82	147.66	147.91	0.67859	0.6774
3- "	99.81	145.82	145.87	0.68713	0.6869
3-Ethylpentane	99.94	143.52	143.85	0.69816	0.6965
2,2-Dimethylpentane	99.81	148.69	148.34	0.67385	0.6755
2,3- "	99.8	144.15	144.15	0.69508	0.6951
2,4- "	99.88	148.95	148.87	0.67270	0.6731
3,3- "	99.78	144.53	144.88	0.69327	0.6916
2,2,3-Trimethylbutane	99.97	145.19	145.24	0.69011	0.6899
n-Octane	99.96	162.59	162.95	0.70252	0.7010
2-Methylheptane ·	99.0	163.66	163.92	0.69792	0.6968
3- "	99.4	161.83	161.99	0.70582	0.7051
4- "	99.85	162.10	161.89	0.70463	0.7056
3-Ethylhexane	—	160.07	159.35	0.71358	0.7146
2,2-Dimethylhexane	99.82	164.28	164.34	0.69528	0.6950
2,3- "	—	160.40	160.50	0.71214	0.7115
2,4- "	—	163.09	162.85	0.70036	0.7014
2,5- "	99.0	164.70	164.88	0.69354	0.6928
3,3-Dimethylhexane	99.88	160.88	160.88	0.71000	0.7100
3,4- "	—	158.81	158.52	0.71923	0.7206
2-Methyl-3-ethylpentane	99.5	158.79	158.52	0.71932	0.7206
3-Methyl-3-ethylpentane	99.5	157.03	157.39	0.72742	0.7257
2,2,3-Trimethylpentane	99.3	159.53	159.21	0.71602	0 7174
2,2,4- "	99.998	165.09	165.31	0.69188	0.6910
2,3,3- "	99.4	157.29	157.75	0.72619	0.7241
2,3,4- "	99.84	158.89	159.03	0.71906	0.7183
2,2,3,3-Tetramethylbutane	—	—	—	—	—
n-Nonane	99.94	178.71	178.96	0.71763	0.7166
2-Methyloctane	99.8	179.76	179.92	0.71346	0.7128
3- "	—	177.952	177.89	0.72070	0.7210

*Equation for calculation (4a): $V_M = \sum\limits_{i \leqslant j=1}^{4} n_{ij} V_{ij}$, constants V_{ij} taken from Table 2.

Equation for calculation (19): $\quad d_4^{20} = \dfrac{M}{\sum\limits_{i \leqslant j=1}^{4} n_{ij} V_{ij}{}^{20}}$

TABLE 13 (contd)

Hydrocarbon	Purity in mol %	V_M^{20}, ml./mole		d_4^{20} g/ml.	
		exp. from [49, 50]	calculated from eq. (4a)	exp. from [49, 50]	calculated from eq. (19)
4-Methyloctane	—	178.14	177.89	0.71990	0.7210
3-Ethylheptane	—	176.40	175.86	0.72600	0.7293
4- "	—	175.68	175.86	0.7300	0.7293
2,2-Dimethylheptane	—	180.50	180.38	0.71050	0.7110
2,3- "	—	176.65	176.54	0.72600	0.7265
2,4- "	—	179.12	178.85	0.71800	0.7171
2,5- "	—	179.37	178.85	0.71500	0.7171
2,6- "	99.6	180.91	180.88	0.70891	0.7090
3,3- "	—	176.75	176.88	0.72560	0.7251
3,4- "	—	175.35	174.51	0.73140	0.7349
3,5- "	—	177.38	176.82	0.72300	0.7253
4,4- "	—	176.89	176.88	0.725	0.725
2-Methyl-3-ethylhexane	—	—	174.51	—	0.7349
3-Methyl-3-ethylhexane	—	—	173.39	—	0.7397
2-Methyl-4- "	—	—	176.82	—	0.7253
3-Methyl-4- "	—	—	172.47	—	0.7436
2,2,3-Trimethylhexane	—	175.87	175.20	0.72920	0.7320
2,2,4- "	—	179.23	179.31	0.71555	0.7152
2,2,5- "	99.86	181.35	181.34	0.70721	0.7072
2,3,3- "	—	173.78	173.74	0.73800	0.7382
2,3,4- "	—	173.49	173.16	0.73920	0.7406
2,3,5- "	—	177.65	177.50	0.72191	0.7225
3,3,4- "	—	172.06	171.71	0.74540	0.7469
3,3,5- "	99.73	177.19	177.86	0.72381	0.7211
3,3-Diethylpentane	99.987	170.19	169.90	0.75359	0.7549
2,2-Dimethyl-3-ethylpentane	—	174.54	173.17	0.73478	0.7406
2,3-Dimethyl-3-ethylpentane	—	—	170.25	—	0.7533
2,4-Dimethyl-3-ethylpentane	—	173.80	173.16	0.73793	0.7406
2,2,3,3-Tetramethylpentane	99.940	169.49	169.70	0.75666	0.7557
2,2,3,4- "	99.976	173.56	173.85	0.73895	0.7377
2,2,4,4- "	99.89	178.26	181.80	0.71947	0.7054
2,3,3,4- "	99.956	169.93	170.60	0.75473	0.7518
n-Decane	99.9	194.93	194.96	0.72987	0.7298
2-Methylnonane	99	195.88	195.92	0.72636	0.7262
3- "	—	193.99	193.89	0.73340	0.7338
4- "	—	194.27	193.89	0.73234	0.7338
5- "	—	194.20	193.89	0.73260	0.7338
3-Ethyloctane	—	192.26	191.86	0.74000	0.7416
4- "	—	192.26	191.86	0.74000	0.7416
2,2-Dimethyloctane	—	196.38	196.38	0.72450	0.7245
2,3- "	—	192.80	192.54	0.73793	0.7389
2,4- "	—	195.86	194.85	0.72640	0.7302
2,5- "	—	193.30	194.85	0.73600	0.7302
2,6- "	—	195.29	194.85	0.72850	0.7302
2,7- "	—	196.45	196.88	0.72420	0.7227
3,3- "	—	192.52	192.89	0.73900	0.7376
3,4- "	—	190.71	190.51	0.74600	0.7468
3,5- "	—	193.30	192.82	0.73600	0.7379
3,6- "	—	193.23	192.82	0.73630	0.7379
4,4- "	—	193.04	192.89	0.73700	0.7376

TABLE 13 (contd.)

Hydrocarbon	Purity in mol %	$V_M{}^{20}$, ml./mole		d_4^{20}, g/ml.	
		exp. from [49, 50]	calculated from eq. (4a)	exp. from [49, 50]	calculated from eq. (19)
4,5-Dimethyloctane	—	190.46	190.51	0.74700	0.7468
2-Methyl-3-ethylheptane	—	—	190.51	—	0.7468
2-Methyl-4- "	—	—	192.81	—	0.7379
2-Methyl-5- "	—	—	192.81	—	0.7379
3-Methyl-3- "	—	—	189.39	—	0.7512
3-Methyl-4-ethylheptane	99	—	188.47	—	0.7549
3-Methyl-5-ethylheptane	—	—	190.78	—	0.7458
4-Methyl-3-ethylheptane	—	—	188.47	—	0.7549
4-Methyl-4-ethylheptane	—	—	189.39	—	0.7512
4-Propylheptane	—	193.33	191.36	0.7359	0.7416
4-Isopropylheptane	—	—	190.51	—	0.7468
2,2,3-Trimethylheptane	—	191.74	191.21	0.7420	0.7441
2,2,4- "	—	195.56	195.31	0.7275	0.7285
2,2,5- "	—	195.97	195.31	0.7260	0.7285
2,2,6- "	—	197.60	197.34	0.7195	0.7210
2,3,3- "	—	190.00	189.74	0.7488	0.7498
2,3,4- "	—	189.44	189.16	0.7510	0.7521
2,3,5- "	—	192.00	191.47	0.7410	0.7431
2,3,6- "	—	193.70	193.50	0.7345	0.7353
2,4,4- "	—	194.10	193.85	0.7330	0.7339
2,4,5- "	—	192.00	191.47	0.7410	0.7431
2,4,6- "	—	196.92	195.81	0.7225	0.7266
3,3,4- "	—	187.94	187.71	0.7570	0.7580
3,3,5- "	—	191.55	191.82	0.7427	0.7417
3,3,6- "	—	193.09	193.85	0.7368	0.7389
3,4,4- "	—	187.94	187.71	0.7510	0.7580
3,4,5- "	—	187.45	187.13	0.7590	0.7603
3,3-Diethylhexane	—	—	185.90	—	0.7653
3,4- "	—	—	186.45	—	0.7631
2,2-Dimethyl-3-ethylhexane	—	—	189.18	—	0.7521
2,2-Dimethyl-4-ethylhexane	—	—	193.28	—	0.7361
2,3-Dimethyl-3-ethylhexane	—	—	186.25	—	0.7639
2,3-Dimethyl-4-ethylhexane	—	—	181.77	—	0.7827
2,4-Dimethyl-3-ethylhexane	—	—	181.77	—	0.7827
2,4-Dimethyl-4-ethylhexane	—	—	190.36	—	0.7474
2,5-Dimethyl-3-ethylhexane	—	—	191.47	—	0.7431
3,3-Dimethyl-4-ethylhexane	—	—	185.68	—	0.7662
3,4-Dimethyl-4-ethylhexane	—	—	184.23	—	0.7723
2-Methyl-3-isopropylhexane	—	—	189.16	—	0.7521
2,2,3,3-Tetramethylhexane	—	186.10	185.71	0.76450	0.7661
2,2,3,4- "	—	188.49	137.82	0.7548	0.7575
2,2,3,5- "	—	192.83	192.17	0.7378	0.7404
2,2,4,4- "	—	190.46	194.31	0.7470	0.7322
2,2,4,5- "	—	193.46	193.96	0.73542	0.7354
2,2,5,5- "	—	197.95	197.80	0.7187	0.7193
2,3,3,4- "	—	184.91	184.57	0.7694	0.7709
2,3,3,5- "	—	190.71	190.70	0.746	0.7461
2,3,4,5- "	—	187.94	187.81	0.757	0.7575
3,3,4,4- "	—	101.85	182.21	0.7824	0.7808
3,3,4,5- "	—	186.24	186.36	0.7639	0.7634

G

TABLE 13 (contd.)

Hydrocarbon	Purity in mol %	V_M^{20}, ml./mole exp. from [49, 50]	V_M^{20}, ml./mole calculated from eq.(4a)	d_4^{20}, g/ml. exp. from [49, 50]	d_4^{20}, g/ml. calculated from eq.(19)
2,2,3-Trimethyl-3-ethylpentane . .	—	—	182.21	—	0.7808
2,2,4-Trimethyl-3-ethylpentane . .	—	—	187.82	—	0.7575
2,3,4-Trimethyl-3-ethylpentane . .	—	183.03	183.11	0,7773	0.7770
2,4-Dimethyl-3-isoprophylpentane .	—	187.63	187.81	0,75826	0.7575
3,3-Diethyl-4-methylpentane . . .	—	—	182.76	—	0.7785
2,2,3,3,4-Pentamethylpentane . . .	—	182.38	182.57	0.78009	0.7793
2,2,3,4,4- " . . .	—	185.49	188.53	0,76702	0.7546
n-Undecane	—	211.17	210.96	0.74017	0.7409
2-Methyldecane	—	—	211.92	—	0.7376
3- "	—	—	209.89	—	0.7447
4- "	—	210.59	209.89	0,7422	0.7447
3-Ethylnonane	—	—	207.86	—	0.7520
4- "	—	—	207.86	—	0.7520
2,2-Dimethylnonane	—	—	212.38	—	0.7360
2,3- "	—	—	208.54	—	0.7495
2,4- "	—	—	210.85	—	0.7413
2,8- "	—	—	212.88	—	0.7342
3,3- "	—	—	208.89	—	0.7483
3,4- "	—	—	206.51	—	0.7569
2,2,7-Trimethyloctane	—	—	213.34	—	0.7326
2,2,3,3-Tetramethyloctane	—	—	201.71	—	0.7749
n-Dodecane	—	227.48	226.96	0,74669	0.7505
2-Methylundecane	—	—	227.92	—	0.7473
3- "	—	—	225.89	—	0.7540
4- "	—	—	225.89	—	0.7540
3-Ethyldecane	—	—	223.86	—	0.7609
4- "	—	—	223.86	—	0.7609
2,2-Dimethyldecane	—	—	228.38	—	0.7458
2,3- "	—	—	224.54	—	0.7586
2,4- "	—	—	226.85	—	0.7508
2,9- "	—	—	228.88	—	0.7442
3,3- "	—	—	224.89	—	0.7574
3,4- "	—	—	222.51	—	0.7655
2,2,8-Trimethylnonane	—	—	229.34	—	0.7427
2,2,3,3-Tetramethyloctane	—	—	217.71	—	0.7824
n-Tridecane	99.7	243.82	242.97	0,7561	0.7588
2-Methyldodecane	—	—	243.93	—	0.7558
3- "	—	—	241.90	—	0.7621
4- "	—	—	241.90	—	0.7621
3-Ethylundecane	—	—	239.87	—	0.7686
4- "	—	—	239.87	—	0.7686
2,2-Dimethylundecane	—	—	244.39	—	0.7543
2,3- "	—	—	240.55	—	0.7664
2,4- "	—	—	242.86	—	0.7591
2,10- "	—	—	244.89	—	0.7528
3,3- "	—	—	240.89	—	0.7653
3,4- "	—	—	238.52	—	0.7729
2,2,9-Trimethyldecane	—	—	245.35	—	0.7514
2,2,3,3-Tetramethylnonane	—	—	233.72	—	0.7888

TABLE 14

Experimental and calculated* values of the molecular refractions R_M^{20} and R_M^{25}

Hydrocarbon	n_D^{20}	R_M^{20}, ml./mole		n_D^{25}	R_M^{25}, ml./mole	
		experimental from [50] and [51]	calculated according to eq. (4b)		experimental from [50] and [51]	calculated according to eq. (4b)
Propane	—	—	15.97	—	—	15.99
n-Butane	—	—	20.62	—	—	20.63
2-Methylpropane	—	—	20.80	—	—	20.83
n-Pentane	1.35745	25.26	25.26	1.35446	25.27	25.27
2-Methylbutane	1.35369	25.29	25.30	1.35084	25.32	25.33
2,2-Dimethylpropane	—	—	25.55	—	—	25.58
n-Hexane	1.37436	29.90	29.91	1.37226	29.93	29.90
2-Methylpentane	1.37145	29.95	29.95	1.36873	29.96	29.96
3- "	1.37652	29.80	29.81	1.37386	29.82	29.82
2,2-Dimethylbutane	1.36876	29.94	29.94	1.36595	—	—
2,3- "	1.37495	29.78	29.83	1.37231	29.83	29.87
n-Heptane	1.38756	34.55	34.55	1.38519	34.48	34.54
2-Methylhexane	1.38485	34.59	34.59	1.38227	34.60	34.60
3- "	1.38864	34.46	34.45	1.38609	34.47	34.46
3-Ethylpentane	1.39339	34.28	34.28	1.39084	34.29	34.32
2,2-Dimethylpentane	1.38215	34.62	34.59	1.37955	34.63	34.61
2,3- "	1.39196	34.32	34.38	1.38945	34.33	34.36
2,4- "	1.38145	34.62	34.63	1.37882	34.63	34.66
3,3- "	1.39092	34.32	34.33	1.38842	34.34	34.35
2,2,3-Trimethylbutane	1.38944	34.37	34.36	1.38692	34.39	34.42
n-Octane	1.39743	39.19	39.20	1.39505	39.21	39.18
2-Methylheptane	1.39494	39.23	39.23	1.39257	39.25	39.21
3- "	1.39848	39.10	39.09	1.39610	39.12	39.09
4- "	1.39792	39.12	39.09	1.39553	39.14	39.09
3-Ethylhexane	1.40162	38.94	38.96	1.39919	38.96	38.96
2,2-Dimethylhexane	1.39349	39.25	39.23	1.39104	39.27	39.24

*Equation for calculation (4b):

$$R_M^- = \sum_{i \leq j=1}^{4} n_{ij} R_{ij},$$ constants R_{ij} taken from Table 3.

TABLE 14 (contd.)

Hydrocarbon	n_D^{20}	R_M^{20}, ml./mole		n_D^{25}	R_M^{25}, ml./mole	
		experimental from [50] and [51]	calculated according to eq. (4b)		experimental from [50] and [51]	calculated according to eq. (4b)
2,3-Dimethylhexane	1.40111	38.98	38.97	1.39880	39.00	39.00
2,4- "	1.39534	39.13	39.13	1.39291	39.15	39.15
2,5- "	1.39246	39.26	39.27	1.39004	39.28	39.30
3,3- "	1.40009	38.99	39.01	1.39782	39.03	38.99
3,4- "	1.40406	38.84	38.82	1.40180	38.87	38.86
2-Methyl-3-ethylpentane . . .	1.40401	38.82	38.82	1.40167	38.86	38.85
3-Methyl-3-ethylpentane . . .	1.40775	38.72	38.71	1.40549	38.73	38.75
2,2,3-Trimethylpentane . . .	1.40295	38.92	38.98	1.40066	38.94	38.92
2,2,4- " . . .	1.39142	39.26	39.27	1.38893	39.23	39.30
2,3,3- " . . .	1.40750	38.76	38.75	1.40522	38.78	38.81
2,3,4- " . . .	1.40422	38.87	38.85	1.40193	38.90	38.90
2,2,3,3-Tetramethylbutane . .	—	—	38.83	—	—	38.89
n-Nonane	1.40542	43.84	43.84	1.40311	43.82	43.82
2-Methyloctane	1.40307	43.89	43.88	1.40079	43.89	43.87
3- "	—	—	43.73	—	—	43.73
4- "	—	—	43.73	—	—	43.73
3-Ethylheptane	—	—	43.59	—	—	43.59
4- "	—	—	43.59	—	—	43.59
2,2-Dimethylheptane	—	—	43.88	—	—	43.88
2,3- "	—	—	43.62	—	—	43.64
2,4- "	—	—	43.77	—	—	43.79
2,5- "	—	—	43.77	—	—	43.79
2,6- "	1.40073	43.93	43.92	—	—	43.93
3,3- "	—	—	43.62	—	—	43.63
3,4- "	—	—	43.47	—	—	43.49
3,5- "	—	—	43.62	—	—	43.65
4,2- "	—	—	43.62	—	—	43.63
2-Methyl-3-ethylhexane . . .	—	—	43.47	—	—	43.49
3-Methyl-3- "	—	—	43.37	—	—	43.38
2-Methyl-4- "	—	—	43.62	—	—	43.65

TABLE 14 (contd.)

Hydrocarbon	n_D^{20}	R_M^{20}, ml./mole		n_D^{25}	R_M^{25}, ml./mole	
		experimental from [50] and [51]	calculated according to eq. (4b)		experimental from [50] and [51]	calculated according to eq. (4b)
3-Methyl-4-ethylhexane . . .	—	—	43.32	—	—	43.35
2,2,3-Trimethylhexane . . .	—	—	43.53	—	—	43.56
2,2,4- " . . .	1.40328	43.76	43.77	1.40095	43.77	43.80
2,2,5- " . . .	1.39972	43.94	43.92	1.39728	43.95	43.94
2,3,3- " . . .	—	—	43.42	—	—	43.45
2,3,4- " . . .	—	—	43.35	—	—	43.40
2,3,5- " . . .	1.40601	43.64	43.66	1.40365	43.66	43.65
3,3,4- " . . .	1.40736	43.30	43.27	—	—	43.30
3,3,5- " . . .	1.40745	43.66	43.66	1.40515	43.67	43.69
3,3-Diethylpentane . . .	1.42051	43.11	43.12	1.41837	43.13	43.12
2,2-Dimethyl-3-ethylpentane .	1.41227	43.45	43.38	1.41014	43.48	43.43
2,3-Dimethyl-3-ethylpentane .	—	—	43.17	—	—	43.19
2,4-Dimethyl-3-ethylpentane .	1.41371	43.40	43.35	1.41146	43.42	43.46
2,2,3,3-Tetramethylpentane .	1.42360	43.20	43.23	1.42140	43.23	43.27
2,2,3,4- " . .	1.41472	43.42	43.41	1.41246	43.45	43.46
2,2,4,4- " . .	1.40694	43.86	43.91	1.40459	44.00	43.95
2,3,3,4- " . .	1.42222	43.20	43.20	1.42003	43.21	43.26
n-Decane	1.41184	48.49	48.49	1.40943	48.45	48.45
2-Methylnonane	1.41000	48.53	48.52	1.40752	48.53	48.51
3- "	—	—	48.38	—	—	48.37
4- "	—	—	48.38	—	—	48.37
5- "	—	—	48.38	—	—	48.37
3-Ethyloctane	—	—	48.23	—	—	48.23
4- "	—	—	48.23	—	—	48.23
2,2-Dimethyloctane	—	—	48.52	—	—	48.52
2,3- "	1.41491	48.26	48.25	1.41266	48.29	48.27
2,4- "	—	—	48.42	—	—	48.43
2,5- "	—	—	48.42	—	—	48.43
2,6- "	—	—	48.42	—	—	48.43
2,7- "	—	—	48.56	—	—	48.57

<u>TABLE 14</u> (contd.)

Hydrocarbon	n_D^{20}	R_M^{20}, ml./mole experimental from [50] and [51]	R_M^{20}, ml./mole calculated according to eq.(4b)	n_D^{25}	R_M^{25}, ml./mole experimental from [50] and [51]	R_M^{25}, ml./mole calculated according to eq. (4b.)
3,3-Dimethyloctane	—	—	48.27	—	—	48.27
3,4- "	—	—	48.11	—	—	48.13
3,5- "	—	—	48.27	—	—	48.29
3,6- "	—	—	48.27	—	—	48.29
4,4- "	—	—	48.27	—	—	48.27
4,5- "	—	—	48.11	—	—	48.13
2-Methyl-3-ethylheptane . . .	—	—	48.11	—	—	48.13
2-Methyl-4- " . . .	—	—	48.27	—	—	48.29
2-Methyl-5- " . . .	—	—	48.27	—	—	48.29
3-Methyl-3- " . . .	—	—	48.02	—	—	48.01
3-Methyl-4- " . . .	—	—	47.97	—	—	47.99
3-Methyl-5- " . . .	—	—	48.12	—	—	48.14
4-Methyl-3- " . . .	—	—	48.02	—	—	48.01
4-Methyl-4- " . . .	—	—	47.97	—	—	47.99
4-Propylheptane	—	—	48.23	—	—	48.23
4-Isopropylheptane	—	—	48.11	—	—	48.13
2,2,3-Trimethylheptane . . .	—	—	48.17	—	—	48.19
2,2,4- " . . .	—	—	48.41	—	—	48.43
2,2,5- " . . .	—	—	48.41	—	—	48.43
2,2,6- " . . .	—	—	48.56	—	—	48.58
2,3,3- " . . .	—	—	48.07	—	—	48.08
2,3,4- " . . .	—	—	48.00	—	—	48.04
2,3,5- " . . .	—	—	48.15	—	—	48.19
2,3,6- " . . .	—	—	48.30	—	—	48.33
2,4,4- " . . .	—	—	48.31	—	—	48.33
2,4,5- " . . .	—	—	48.15	—	—	48.19
2,4,6- " . . .	—	—	48.45	—	—	48.49
3,3,4- " . . .	—	—	47.92	—	—	47.94
3,3,5- " . . .	1.41701	48.17	48.16	—	—	48.18
3,3,6- " . . .	—	—	48.31	—	—	48.33
3,4,4-Trimethylheptane . . .	—	—	47.92	—	—	47.94

TABLE 14 (contd.)

Hydrocarbon	n_D^{20}	R_M^{20}, ml./mole experimental from [52] and [51]	R_M^{20}, ml./mole calculated according to eq. (4b)	n_D^{25}	R_M^{25}, ml./mole experimental from [50] and [51]	R_M^{25}, ml./mole calculated according to eq. (4b)
3,4,5-Trimethylheptane	—	—	47.85	—	—	47.89
3,3-Diethylhexane	—	—	47.76	—	—	47.76
3,4- "	—	—	47.82	—	—	47.84
2,2-Dimethyl-3-ethylhexane . .	—	—	48.03	—	—	48.05
2,2-Dimethyl-4-ethylhexane . .	—	—	48.27	—	—	48.29
2,3-Dimethyl-3-ethylhexane . .	—	—	47.81	—	—	47.83
2,3-Dimethyl-4- " . .	—	—	47.85	—	—	47.89
2,4-Dimethyl-3- " . .	—	—	47.85	—	—	47.89
2,4-Dimethyl-4- " . .	—	—	48.05	—	—	48.07
2,5-Dimethyl-3- " . .	—	—	48.15	—	—	48.19
3,3-Dimethyl-4- " . .	—	—	47.77	—	—	47.80
3,4-Dimethyl-4- " . .	—	—	47.66	—	—	47.69
2-Methyl-3-isopropylhexane . .	—	—	48.00	—	—	48.04
2,2,3,3-Tetramethylhexane . .	1.42812	47.88	47.87	1.42606	47.92	47.91
2,2,3,4- " . . .	—	—	47.91	—	—	47.95
2,2,3,5- " . . .	—	—	48.21	—	—	48.25
2,2,4,4- " . . .	—	—	48.31	—	—	48.33
2,2,4,5- " . . .	1.41321	48.26	48.30	1.41093	48.28	48.34
2,2,5,5- " . . .	1.40550	48.57	48.56	1.40315	48.59	48.58
2,3,3,4- " . . .	—	—	47.71	—	—	47.76
2,3,3,5- " . . .	—	—	48.10	—	—	48.14
2,3,4,5- " . . .	—	—	47.88	—	—	47.94
3,3,4,4- " . . .	—	—	47.62	—	—	47.66
3,3,4,5- " . . .	—	—	47.80	—	—	47.85
2,2,3-Trimethyl-3-ethylpentane .	—	—	47.62	—	—	47.66
2,2,4-Trimethyl-3-ethylpentane .	—	—	47.91	—	—	47.95
2,3,4-Trimethyl-3-ethylpentane .	—	—	47.61	—	—	47.65
2,4-Dimethyl-3-isopropylpentane .	1.42465	47.94	47.88	1.42246	47.96	47.94
3,3-Diethyl-4-methylpentane . .	—	—	47.56	—	—	47.58
2,2,3,3,4-Pentamethylpentane . .	1.43606	47.67	47.67	1.43412	47.71	47.73
2,2,3,4,4-Pentamethylpentane . .	1.43069	47.97	47.95	1.42868	48.00	48.02

TABLE 15

Experimental and calculated* values of λ° for various temperature ranges, in cal/mole

Hydrocarbon	40—80° C		70—110° C		90—130° C		110—150° C		130—170° C	
	$\lambda°$ exp.	$\lambda°$calc.	$\lambda°$ exp.	$\lambda°$ calc.	$\lambda°$ exp.	$\lambda°$ calc.	$\lambda°$ exp.	$\lambda°$calc.	$\lambda°$ exp.	$\lambda°$ calc.
n-Hexane	1613.4	1624.2	1565.2	1574.4	1540.2	1547.5	1518.0	1524.6	1513.5	1504.2
2-Methylpentane	1537.0	1535.5	1495.7	1494.9	1471.7	1471.9	1464.3	1457.6	1474.4	1434.8
3— "	1558.7	1530.2	1512.8	1498.1	1489.7	1475.2	1471.3	1455.8	1474.2	1435.2
2,2-Dimethylbutane	1435.3	1409.0	1399.6	1392.8	1361.6	1374.5	1336.2	1358.0	1368.8	1347.5
2,3— "	1500.9	1500.5	1463.5	1457.5	1441.9	1436.7	1427.8	1420.6	1436.8	1401.9
n-Heptane	1839.3	1851.6	1778.4	1785.2	1744.4	1749.6	1714.7	1718.8	1682.8	1691.6
2-Methylhexane	1759.6	1762.9	1703.2	1705.7	1672.8	1674.0	1646.5	1651.8	1635.6	1622.2
2,2-Dimethylpentane	1648.3	1636.4	1601.3	1603.6	1573.9	1576.2	1549.8	1552.2	1532.3	1534.9
2,3— "	1732.9	1722.6	1681.4	1671.5	1652.5	1642.1	1627.2	1617.2	1604.9	1589.3
2,4— "	1670.8	1674.2	1621.1	1626.2	1503.4	1598.4	1568.9	1576.4	1536.0	1552.8
3,3— "	1677.9	1554.0	1631.7	1614.0	1606.2	1589.4	1587.1	1567.2	1562.9	1549.8
2,2,3-Trimethylbutane	1630.7	1622.7	1587.1	1583.8	1562.7	1560.8	1538.4	1543.2	1525.9	1523.6
3-Ethylpentane . .	1776.8	1752.3	1721.6	1712.1	1690.5	1680.6	—	—	—	—
n-Octane	2075.2	2079.0	1995.5	1996.0	1951.5	1951.7	1913.1	1913.0	1879.5	1879.0
2-Methylheptane	1985.6	1990.3	1915.5	1916.5	1876.5	1876.1	1842.4	1846.0	1812.7	1809.6
3— "	1995.6	1985.0	1923.0	1919.7	1883.1	1879.4	1848.1	1844.2	1816.9	1810.0
4— "	1987.4	1985.0	1915.6	1919.7	1875.9	1879.4	1840.7	1844.2	1810.4	1810.0

*Equation for calculation (4d):

$$\lambda° = \sum_{i \leqslant j = 1}^{4} n_{ij} \lambda_{ij},$$

constants λ_{ij} being taken from Table 5.

TABLE 15 (contd.)

Hydrocarbon	40—80° C λ° exp.	40—80° C λ° calc.	70—110° C λ° exp.	70—110° C λ° calc.	90—130° C λ° exp.	90—130° C λ° calc.	110—150° C λ° exp.	110—150° C λ° calc.	130—170° C λ° exp.	130—170° C λ° calc.
3-Ethylhexane	1987.6	1979.7	1915.7	1922.9	1875.7	1882.7	1840.6	1846.6	1810.5	1810.4
2,2-Dimethylhexane . .	1871.8	1863.8	1807.6	1814.4	1771.8	1778.7	1740.3	1746.4	1713.6	1722.3
2,3— "	1946.5	1950.0	1878.2	1882.3	1840.4	1844.2	1807.3	1811.4	1777.8	1780.3
2,4— "	1896.9	1896.3	1831.1	1840.2	1794.7	1803.8	1763.1	1773.0	1734.7	1740.4
2,5— "	1901.1	1901.6	1834.9	1837.0	1798.0	1800.5	1765.7	1770.6	1737.3	1740.0
3,3— "	1889.5	1881.4	1827.5	1824.8	1793.1	1791.5	1762.9	1761.4	1736.1	1737.2
3,4— "	1957.8	1944.7	1890.2	1885.5	1852.6	1847.5	1819.7	1817.8	1790.8	1780.7
2-Methyl-3-ethylpentane	1933.9	1944.7	1867.8	1885.5	1831.0	1847.5	1799.0	1817.8	1770.5	1780.7
3-Methyl-3— "	1915.0	1898.9	1855.2	1835.2	1821.8	1804.3	1792.3	1776.4	1766.8	1752.1
2,2,3-Trimethylpentane	1857.4	1844.8	1797.8	1798.1	1764.6	1766.2	1735.3	1739.8	1709.9	1707.3
2,2,4— "	1774.5	1775.5	1720.4	1734.9	1690.2	1703.1	1663.4	1679.2	1640.4	1652.8
2,3,3— "	1878.3	1867.7	1820.6	1805.0	1788.4	1775.7	1760.5	1752.2	1735.0	1721.8
2,3,4— "	1898.7	1915.0	1836.5	1844.9	1801.9	1809.0	1771.9	1778.6	1744.8	1750.7
n-Nonane	2323.0	2306.4	2220.1	2206.8	2163.6	2153.8	2114.6	2107.2	2072.2	2066.4
2-Methyloctane . . .	2214.5	2217.7	2129.7	2127.3	2083.1	2078.8	2042.9	2040.2	2006.2	1996.9
2,2,5-Trimethylhexane .	2009.1	2002.5	1933.9	1945.7	1892.3	1905.2	1855.8	1869.4	1824.0	1840.2
2,4,4— "	2026.6	2020.7	1955.7	1956.1	1916.2	1918.0	1881.7	1888.4	1851.1	1855.1
3,3-Diethylpentane . .	2125.0	2143.9	2052.9	2056.4	2012.6	2019.2	1977.4	1985.6	1946.4	1954.1
2,2,3,4-Tetramethylpentane	2024.3	2034.5	1953.8	1971.2	1915.1	1933.1	1881.0	1897.0	1851.4	1869.1
2,2,4,4— "	1910.3	1876.0	1868.2	1843.6	1831.9	1807.8	1800.2	1774.0	1772.2	1753.0
2,3,3,4— "	2088.9	2081.4	2016.5	1996.0	1976.3	1962.0	1941.1	1957.6	1910.2	1901.8

TABLE 16

Experimental and calculated* values of the latent heat of vaporization L° for different temperature ranges, in cal/mole

Hydrocarbon	40—80° C		70—110° C		90—130° C		110—150° C		130—170° C	
	L° exp.	L° calc.	L° exp.	L°calc.	L° exp.	L° calc.	L° exp.	L° calc.	L° exp.	L° calc.
n-Hexane	7381.3	7430.7	7160.8	7202.9	7046.4	7079.8	6944.8	6975.0	6924.3	6881.7
2-Methylpentane	7031.8	7024.9	6842.8	6839.2	6733.0	6733.9	6699.2	6668.5	6745.4	6564.2
3- "	7131.1	7000.7	6921.1	6853.8	6815.4	6749.0	6731.2	6660.3	6744.5	6566.0
2,2-Dimethylbutane	6566.5	6446.2	6403.2	6372.1	6229.3	6288.3	6113.1	6212.8	6262.3	6164.8
2,3- "	6866.6	6864.8	6695.5	6668.1	6596.7	6572.9	6532.2	6499.2	6573.4	6413.7
n-Heptane	8643.5	8471.1	8136.2	8167.3	7980.6	8004.4	7844.8	7863.5	7698.8	7739.1
2-Methylhexane	8050.2	8065.3	7792.1	7803.6	7653.1	7658.5	7532.7	7557.0	7482.9	7421.6
2,2-Dimethylpentane	7541.0	7486.5	7325.9	7336.5	7200.6	7211.1	7090.3	7101.3	7010.3	7022.2
2,3- "	7928.0	7880.9	7692.4	7647.1	7560.2	7512.6	7444.4	7401.9	7342.4	7271.0
2,4- "	7643.9	7659.5	7416.5	7439.9	7289.8	7312.7	7177.7	7212.0	7027.2	7104.1
3,3- "	7676.4	7567.0	7465.0	7384.0	7348.4	7271.5	7261.0	7169.9	7150.3	7090.3
3-Ethylpentane	8128.9	8016.8	7876.3	7832.9	7734.0	7688.7				—
2,2,3-Trimethylbutane	7460.5	7423.9	7261.0	7245.9	7149.4	7140.7	7038.2	7060.1	6981.0	6970.5
n-Octane	9494.0	9511.4	9129.4	9131.7	8928.1	8929.0	8752.4	8752.0	8598.7	8596.4
2-Methylheptane	9084.1	9105.6	8763.4	8768.0	8585.0	8583.2	8429.0	8445.4	8293.1	8278.9
3- "	9129.9	9081.4	8797.7	8782.6	8615.2	8598.3	8455.1	8437.2	8312.3	8280.7
4- "	9092.4	9081.4	8763.9	8782.6	8582.2	8598.3	8421.2	8437.2	8282.6	8280.7
3-Ethylhexane	9093.3	9057.1	8764.3	8797.3	8581.3	8613.4	8420.7	8448.2	8283.0	8282.6
2,2-Dimethylhexane	8563.5	8526.9	8269.8	8300.9	8106.0	8138.0	7961.9	7989.8	7839.7	7879.5
2,3- "	8905.2	8921.2	8592.8	8611.5	8419.8	8437.2	8268.4	8287.2	8133.4	8144.9
2,4- "	8678.3	8675.6	8377.3	8418.9	8210.8	8252.4	8066.2	8111.5	7936.3	7962.3
2,5- "	8697.5	8699.8	8394.7	8404.3	8225.9	8237.3	8078.1	8100.5	7948.1	7960.5
3,3- "	8644.5	8607.4	8360.8	8348.5	8203.4	8196.1	8065.3	8058.4	7942.7	7947.7
3,4- "	8956.9	8897.0	8647.7	8626.2	8471.1	8452.3	8325.1	8316.4	8192.9	8146.7

*Equation for calculation (4c):

$$L° = \sum_{i<j=1}^{4} n_{ij} L_{ij} ,$$

constants L_{ij} being taken from Table 4.

TABLE 16 (contd.)

Hydrocarbon	40—80° C		70—110° C		90—130° C		110—150° C		130—170° C	
	L° exp.	L° calc.	L° exp.	L° calc.	L° exp.	L° calc.	L° exp.	L° calc.	L° exp.	L° calc.
2-Methyl-3-ethylpentane	8847.6	8897.0	8545.2	8626.2	8376.8	8452.3	8230.4	8316.4	8100.0	8146.7
3-Methyl-3- "	8761.1	8687.5	8487.5	8396.0	8334.7	8254.7	8199.8	8127.0	8083.1	8015.9
2,2,3-Trimethylpentane	8497.6	8440.0	8224.9	8226.3	8073.0	8080.4	7939.0	7959.6	7822.8	7810.9
2,2,4- "	8118.3	8122.9	7870.8	7937.2	7732.7	7791.7	7610.1	7682.3	7504.8	7561.6
2,3,3- "	8593.2	8544.7	8329.2	8257.9	8181.9	8123.8	8054.3	8016.3	7937.6	7877.2
2,3,4- "	8686.6	8761.1	8402.0	8440.4	8234.5	8267.0	8106.4	8137.1	7982.5	8009.5
n-Nonane	10628.0	10552.0	10157.0	10096.0	9898.0	9854.0	9674.0	9640.0	9480.0	9454.0
2-Methyloctane	10131.0	10146.0	9743.0	9732.0	9530.0	9508.0	9346.0	9315.0	9178.0	9136.0
3- "	—	10122.0	—	9747.0	—	9523.0	—	9326.0	—	9138.0
4- "	—	10122.0	—	9747.0	—	9523.0	—	9326.0	—	9138.0
3-Ethylheptane	—	10098.0	—	9762.0	—	9538.0	—	9337.0	—	9140.0
4- "	—	10098.0	—	9762.0	—	9538.0	—	9337.0	—	9140.0
2,2-Dimethylheptane	—	9567.0	—	9265.0	—	9062.0	—	8878.0	—	8737.0
2,3- "	—	9962.0	—	9576.0	—	9362.0	—	9176.0	—	8988.0
2,4- "	—	9716.0	—	9383.0	—	9177.0	—	9000.0	—	8821.0
2,5- "	—	9716.0	—	9383.0	—	9177.0	—	9000.0	—	8821.0
2,6- "	—	9740.0	—	9369.0	—	9162.0	—	8989.0	—	8819.0
3,3- "	—	9648.0	—	9313.0	—	9121.0	—	8947.0	—	8805.0
3,4- "	—	9937.0	—	9591.0	—	9377.0	—	9187.0	—	8989.0
3,5- "	—	9692.0	—	9398.0	—	9192.0	—	9011.0	—	8822.0
4,4- "	—	9647.8	—	9303.7	—	9102.4	—	8946.9	—	8805.0
2-Methyl-3-ethylhexane	—	9937.4	—	9581.4	—	9358.6	—	9186.6	—	8989.4
3-Methyl-3- "	—	9728.3	—	9351.3	—	9161.0	—	9015.5	—	8873.2
2-Methyl-4- "	—	9691.7	—	9388.8	—	9173.8	—	9010.9	—	8822.4
2-Methyl-4-ethylhexane	—	9904.0	—	9596.1	—	9373.7	—	9197.6	—	8991.2
2,2,3-Trimethylhexane	9192.0	9459.3	8848.0	9180.2	8657.0	8986.7	8490.0	8828.8	8345.0	8687.0
2,2,4- "	—	9128.0	—	8907.1	—	8713.1	—	8563.5	—	8421.2
2,2,5- "	—	9152.3	—	8883.3	—	8698.0	—	8552.5	—	8419.4
2,3,3- "	—	9564.0	—	9204.0	—	9030.1	—	8886.5	—	8753.3
2,3,4- "	—	9768.1	—	9401.2	—	9197.6	—	9036.5	—	8838.9

TABLE 16 (contd.)

Hydrocarbon	40—80°C		70—110°C		90—130°C		110—150°C		130—170°C	
	L° exp.	L°calc.	L° exp.	L° calc.	L° exp.	L° calc.	L° exp.	L° calc.	L° exp.	L° calc.
2,4,4-Trimethylhexane	9272.0	9233.0	8947.0	8831.0	8767.0	8757.0	8609.0	8621.0	8469.0	8488.0
2,3,5- "	—	9547.0	—	9194.0	—	8998.0	—	8850.0	—	8670.0
3,3,4- "	—	9540.0	—	9219.0	—	9045.0	—	8898.0	—	8755.0
3,3-Diethylpentane	9722.0	9800.0	9392.0	9390.0	9208.0	9220.0	9047.0	9084.0	8905.0	8941.0
2,2-Dimethyl-3-ethylpentane	—	9435.0	—	9185.7	—	9001.8	—	8839.8	—	8688.8
2,3-Dimethyl-3- "	—	9644.6	—	9251.6	—	9088.7	—	8955.1	—	8821.5
2,4-Dimethyl-3- "	—	9768.1	—	9401.2	—	9197.6	—	9036.5	—	8838.9
2,2,3,3-Tetramethylpentane	—	—	—	—	—	—	—	—	—	—
2,2,3,4- "	9261.0	9299.1	8939.0	8999.9	8762.0	8825.6	8606.0	8678.8	8470.0	8536.5
2,2,4,4- "	8740.0	8573.5	8547.0	8416.2	8381.0	8252.4	8236.0	8116.1	8108.0	8020.0
2,3,3,4- "	9557.0	9488.5	9225.0	9113.4	9042.0	8957.8	8881.0	8826.1	8739.0	8701.6
n-Decane	—	11592.4	—	11060.4	—	10781.8	—	10529.1	—	10211.4
2-Methylnonane	—	11186.6	—	10696.7	—	10434.1	—	10203.4	—	9993.9
3- "	—	11162.2	—	10711.3	—	10451.0	—	10214.3	—	9995.7
4- "	—	11162.2	—	10711.3	—	10451.0	—	10214.3	—	9995.7
5- "	—	11162.2	—	10711.3	—	10451.0	—	10214.3	—	9995.7
3-Ethyloctane	—	11137.8	—	10725.9	—	10467.9	—	10225.2	—	9997.5
4- "	—	11137.8	—	10725.9	—	10467.9	—	10225.2	—	9997.5
2,2-Dimethyloctane	—	10607.7	—	10229.6	—	9988.6	—	9766.7	—	9594.3
2,3- "	—	11002.2	—	10540.3	—	10288.2	—	10064.3	—	9845.1
2,4- "	—	10756.4	—	10347.6	—	10103.3	—	9888.6	—	9678.2
2,5- "	—	10756.4	—	10347.6	—	10103.3	—	9888.6	—	9678.2
2,6- "	—	10756.4	—	10347.6	—	10103.3	—	9888.6	—	9678.2
2,7- "	—	10780.8	—	10333.1	—	10076.4	—	9877.7	—	9676.4
3,3- "	—	10688.2	—	10277.2	—	10049.0	—	9835.3	—	9662.4
3,4- "	—	10977.8	—	10554.9	—	10305.1	—	10075.3	—	9846.9
3,5- "	—	10732.0	—	10352.2	—	10120.2	—	9899.5	—	9680.0
3,6- "	—	10732.0	—	10352.2	—	10120.2	—	9899.5	—	9680.0
4,4- "	—	10688.2	—	10277.2	—	10049.0	—	9835.3	—	9662.4
4,5- "	—	10977.8	—	10554.9	—	10305.1	—	10075.2	—	9846.9
2-Methyl-3-ethylheptane	—	10977.8	—	10554.9	—	10305.1	—	10075.2	—	9846.9

TABLE 16 (contd.)

Hydrocarbon	40—80° C		70—110° C		90—130° C		110—150° C		130—170° C	
	$L°$ exp.	$L°$ calc.	$L°$ exp.	$L°$ calc.	$L°$ exp.	$L°$ calc.	$L°$ exp.	$L°$ calc.	$L°$ exp.	$L°$ calc.
2-Methyl-3-ethylheptane	—	10732.0	—	10352.2	—	10120.2	—	9899.5	—	9680.0
2-Methyl-5— "	—	10732.0	—	10352.2	—	10120.2	—	9899.5	—	9680.0
3-Methyl-3— "	—	10758.7	—	10324.8	—	10109.4	—	9903.9	—	9730.5
3-Methyl-4— "	—	10430.4	—	10569.5	—	10322.0	i	10086.1	—	9848.7
3-Methyl-5— "	—	10707.6	—	10376.8	—	10137.1	—	9910.4	—	9681.8
4-Methyl-4— "	—	10758.7	—	10324.8	—	10109.4	—	9903.9	—	9730.5
4-Propylheptane	—	11137.8	—	10725.9	—	10467.9	—	10225.2	—	9997.5
4-Isopropylheptane	—	10977.8	—	10554.9	—	10305.1	—	10075.2	—	9846.9
2,2,3-Trimethylheptane	—	10508.8	—	10153.6	—	9931.4	—	9718.3	—	9544.4
2,2,4— "	—	10177.5	—	9880.5	—	9657.8	—	9451.9	—	9278.6
2,2,5— "	—	10177.5	—	9880.5	—	9657.8	—	9451.9	—	9278.6
2,2,6— "	—	10201.9	—	9865.9	—	9640.9	—	9441.0	—	9276.8
2,3,4— "	—	10613.7	—	10186.6	—	9974.9	—	9775.0	—	9610.7
2,3,5— "	—	10817.8	—	10383.9	—	10142.3	—	9925.2	—	9696.3
2,3,6— "	—	10572.0	—	10191.2	—	9957.4	—	9749.5	—	9529.4
2,4,4— "	—	10596.4	—	10176.6	—	9940.5	—	9738.6	—	9527.6
2,4,5— "	—	10282.4	—	9913.5	—	9701.3	—	9509.6	—	9345.9
2,4,6— "	—	10572.0	—	10121.2	—	9957.4	—	9749.5	—	9529.4
3,3,4— "	—	10350.6	—	9983.9	—	9755.6	—	9562.9	—	9360.7
3,3,5— "	—	10589.3	—	10201.2	—	9991.8	—	9785.9	—	9612.5
3,4,4— "	—	10258.0	—	9928.1	—	9718.2	—	9520.5	—	9346.7
3,4,5— "	—	10282.4	—	9913.5	—	9701.3	—	9509.6	—	9345.9
3,3-Diethylhexane	—	10589.3	—	10201.2	—	9991.8	—	9785.9	—	9612.5
3,4— "	—	10793.4	—	10398.5	—	10159.2	—	9936.1	—	9698.1
2,2-Dimethyl-3-ethyl-hexane	—	10849.2	—	10372.4	—	10169.8	—	9972.5	—	9798.6
2,2-Dimethyl-4— "	—	10929.0	—	10584.1	—	10338.9	—	10097.0	—	9850.5
2,3-Dimethyl-3— "	—	10484.4	—	10168.2	—	9955.5	—	9728.2	—	9546.2
2,3-Dimethyl-4— "	—	10153.1	—	9895.1	—	9681.9	—	9462.8	—	9280.4
2,4-Dimethyl-3— "	—	10694.2	—	10234.2	—	10035.3	—	9843.6	—	9678.8
	—	10793.4	—	10398.5	—	10159.2	—	9936.1	—	9698.1
	—	10793.4	—	10398.5	—	10159.2	—	9936.1	—	9698.1

TABLE 16 (contd.)

Hydrocarbon	40—80° C		70—110° C		90—130° C		110—150° C		130—170° C	
	$L°$ exp.	$L°$ calc.	$L°$ exp.	$L°$ calc.	$L°$ exp.	$L°$ calc.	$L°$ exp.	$L°$ calc.	$L°$ exp.	$L°$ calc.
2,4-Dimethyl-4-ethylhexane	—	10362.9	—	9961.1	—	9761.7	—	9578.2	—	9413.0
2,5-Dimethyl-3- "	—	10572.0	—	10191.2	—	9957.4	—	9749.5	—	9529.4
3,3-Dimethyl-4- "	—	10564.9	—	10215.8	—	10008.7	—	9796.8	—	9614.3
3,4-Dimethyl-4- "	—	10669.8	—	10248.8	—	10052.2	—	9854.5	—	9680.6
2-Methyl-3-isopropyl-hexane	—	10817.8	—	10344.5	—	10442.3	—	9925.2	—	9696.3
2,2,3,3-Tetramethylhexane	—	10324.8	—	9997.2	—	9785.5	—	9533.0	—	9395.6
2,2,3,4- "	—	10103.0	—	9789.9	—	9583.7	—	9391.6	—	9226.9
2,2,3,5- "	—	9703.5	—	9446.4	—	9255.8	—	9072.9	—	8945.3
2,2,4,4- "	—	10017.4	—	9709.5	—	9495.0	—	9301.9	—	9128.0
2,2,4,5- "	—	9623.0	—	9398.8	—	9195.4	—	9004.3	—	8877.2
2,2,5,5- "	—	10515.0	—	10111.0	—	9918.0	—	9726.0	—	9561.0
2,3,3,4- "	—	10208.0	—	9822.9	—	9627.2	—	9449.3	—	9293.2
2,3,3,5- "	—	10657.8	—	10212.9	—	9979.5	—	9775.2	—	9545.7
2,3,4,5- "	—	—	—	—	—	—	—	—	—	—
3,3,4,4- "	—	—	—	—	—	—	—	—	—	—
3,3,4,5- "	—	—	—	—	—	—	—	—	—	—
2,2,3-Trimethyl-3-ethyl-pentane	—	10429.3	—	10030.2	—	9832.6	—	9635.9	—	9461.9
2,2,4- "	—	—	—	—	—	—	—	—	—	—
2,3,4- "	—	10324.4	—	9997.2	—	9789.1	—	9578.2	—	9395.6
2,4-Dimethyl-3-isopropyl-pentane	—	10619.7	—	10143.6	—	9961.2	—	9783.3	—	9627.1
3,3-Diethyl-4-methyl-pentane	—	10657.8	—	10212.9	—	9979.5	—	9775.2	—	9545.7
2,2,3,3,4-Pentamethyl-pentane	—	10474.7	—	10281.8	—	10106.5	—	9912.2	—	9746.9
2,2,3,4,4-Pentamethyl-pentane	—	9855.4	—	9505.9	—	9411.8	—	9220.2	—	9093.1

TABLE 17

Experimental and calculated* values of b for different temperature ranges

Hydrocarbon	40—80° C		70—110° C		90—130° C		110—150° C		130—170° C	
	b exp.	b calc.	b exp.	b calc.	b exp.	b calc.	b exp.	b calc.	b exp.	b calc.
n-Hexane . . .	7.5889	7.6023	7.4586	7.4630	7.3916	7.3914	7.3352	7.3326	7.3256	7.4281
2-Methylpentane .	7.4871	7.4723	7.3687	7.3585	7.3046	7.2987	7.2869	7.2496	7.3112	7.3492
3- "	7.4957	7.4426	7.3786	7.3567	7.3167	7.2951	7.2702	7.2455	7.2783	7.3429
2,2-Dimethylbutane .	7.3237	7.2472	7.1944	7.1997	7.1182	7.1491	7.0556	7.1058	7.1360	7.2294
2,3- "	7.4103	7.4126	7.3029	7.2881	7.2454	7.2362	7.2098	7.1917	7.2326	7.3023
n-Heptane . . .	7.8388	7.8662	7.6643	7.6798	7.5732	7.5850	7.4980	7.5066	7.4207	7.4384
2-Methylhexane .	7.7289	7.7367	7.5671	7.5753	7.5045	7.4923	7.4190	7.4236	7.3935	7.3595
2,2-Dimethylpentane	7.5579	7.5111	7.4231	7.4165	7.3498	7.3427	7.2886	7.2798	7.2466	7.2397
2,3- "	7.6590	7.6463	7.5107	7.5031	7.4506	7.4267	7.3693	7.3616	7.3152	7.3063
2,4- "	7.6048	7.6072	7.6624	7.4708	7.3881	7.3992	7.3260	7.3406	7.2458	7.2501
3,3- "	7.5530	7.5036	7.4207	7.3988	7.3525	7.3302	7.3040	7.2738	7.2449	7.2314
3-Ethylpentane .	7.7319	7.6763	7.5736	7.5717	7.4905	7.4859				—
2,2,3-Trimethylbutane .	7.4866	7.4623	7.3615	7.3612	7.2963	7.2958	7.2345	7.2404	7.2050	7.2010
n-Octane . . .	8.1186	8.1301	7.8901	7.8966	7.7723	7.7786	7.6749	7.6806	7.5938	7.5961
2-Methylheptane .	7.9852	8.0006	7.7841	7.7921	7.6800	7.6859	7.5834	7.5976	7.5216	7.5172
3- "	7.9959	7.9704	7.7879	7.7903	7.6812	7.6826	7.5923	7.5935	7.5169	7.5109
4- "	7.9897	7.9704	7.7837	7.7903	7.6776	7.6826	7.5882	7.5935	7.5151	7.5109

*Equation for calculation (4e):

$$b = \sum_{i,\,j=1}^{n} n_{ij} b_{ij},$$

constants b_{ij} being taken from Table 6.

TABLE 17 (contd.)

Hydrocarbon	40—80° C		70—110° C		90—130° C		110—150° C		130—170° C	
	b exp.	b calc.	b exp.	b calc.	b exp.	b calc.	b exp.	b calc.	b exp.	b calc.
3-Ethylhexane . . .	7.9802	7.9402	7.7739	7.7885	7.6672	7.6795	7.5780	7.5894	7.5052	7.5046
2,2-Dimethylhexane	7.8207	7.7750	7.6365	7.6333	7.5406	7.5363	7.4608	7.4538	7.3963	7.3974
2,3- "	7.9090	7.9102	7.7132	7.7199	7.6122	7.6203	7.5281	7.5356	7.4568	7.4540
2,4- """	7.8549	7.8409	7.6663	7.6858	7.5688	7.5889	7.4887	7.5105	7.4091	7.4320
2,5- "	7.8700	7.8711	7.6803	7.6876	7.5817	7.5928	7.4995	7.5146	7.4310	7.4383
3,3- "	7.8038	7.7675	7.6260	7.6156	7.5341	7.5238	7.4573	7.4478	7.3927	7.3891
3,4- "	7.9124	7.8800	7.7193	7.7181	7.6180	7.6172	7.5345	7.5315	7.4645	7.4577
2-Methyl-3-ethylpentane	7.8755	7.8800	7.6857	7.7181	7.5874	7.6172	7.5063	7.5315	7.4373	7.4577
3-Methyl-3- "	7.7938	7.7600	7.6223	7.5959	7.5329	7.5119	7.4582	7.4418	7.3966	7.3808
2,2,3-Trimethylpentane	7.7454	7.7345	7.5743	7.5762	7.4855	7.4863	7.4111	7.4103	7.3499	7.3522
2,2,4- "	7.6536	7.6455	7.4982	7.5288	7.4175	7.4436	7.3495	7.3708	7.2941	7.3190
2,3,3- "	7.7404	7.7572	7.5747	7.5593	7.4888	7.4769	7.4179	7.4084	7.3563	7.3502
2,3,4- "	7.8097	7.8500	7.6314	7.6495	7.5389	7.5580	7.4626	7.4777	7.3971	7.4171
n-Nonane	8.4387	8.3940	8.1436	8.1134	7.9927	7.9722	7.8681	7.8546	7.7660	7.7538
2-Methyloctane . .	8.2549	8.2645	8.0116	8.0089	7.8870	7.8795	7.7851	7.5976	7.6964	7.6749
2,2,5-Trimethylhexane	7.9696	7.9094	7.7538	7.7456	7.6426	7.6372	7.5501	7.5455	7.4733	7.4784
2,4,4- "	7.9349	7.9019	7.7314	7.7269	7.6256	7.0247	7.5382	7.5394	7.4643	7.4679
3,3-Diethylpentane .	7.9994	8.0164	7.7923	7.7940	7.6846	7.6924	7.5953	7.6092	7.5204	7.5302
2,2,3,4-Tetramethylpentane	7.9017	7.9382	7.6996	7.7226	7.5960	7.6176	7.5095	7.5260	7.4379	7.4632
2,2,4,4- "	7.7147	7.6838	7.6086	7.5868	7.5116	7.4876	7.4311	7.4012	7.3635	7.3566
2,3,3,4- "	7.9640	8.0108	7.7565	7.7208	7.6489	7.6236	7.5597	7.5422	7.4849	7.4692

TABLE 18

Experimental and calculated* values of Δ Z° (el., gas) Δ H (comb., liq.) and Δ H (el., gas) of alkanes in kcal/mole

Hydrocarbon	ΔZ° (el., gas) T = 298.16° K		ΔZ° (el., gas) T = 500° K		ΔZ° (el., gas) T = 700° K		ΔH (comb., liq.) T = 298.16° K		ΔH (el., gas) T = 298.16° K	
	experimental from [50]	calculated from eq. (4g)*	experimental from [50]	calculated from eq. (4g)*	experimental from [50]	calculated from eq. (4g)*	experimental from [50]	calculated from eq. (4g)*	experimental from [50]	calculated from eq. (4g)*
Propane . . .	−5.61	−6.26	8.23	7.55	22.93	22.19	−526.78 ± 0.133	−526.48	−24.82 ± 0.14	−25.08
n-Butane . .	−4.10	−4.23	14.54	14.44	34.19	34.10	−682.84 ± 0.167	−682.71	−30.37 ± 0.16	−30.04
2-Methylpropane .	−5.0	−5.49	14.39	13.78	34.74	33.98	−681.63 ± 0.151	−680.98	−32.42 ± 0.13	−32.37
n-Pentane . .	−2.00	−2.21	21.51	21.33	46.20	46.00	−838.80 ± 0.14	−838.94	−35.00 ± 0.16	−35.00
2-Methylbutane .	−3.54	−2.98	20.26	21.06	45.19	46.23	−837.30 ± 0.18	−837.68	−36.92 ± 0.20	−36.70
2,2-Dimethylpropane .	−3.64	−4.34	21.89	21.10	48.46	47.44	−835.18 ± 0.24	−834.72	−39.67 ± 0.25	−40.12
n-Hexane . .	−0.07	−0.18	28.30	28.22	57.98	57.91	−995.01 ± 0.17	−995.17	−39.96 ± 0.19	−39.96
2-Methylpentane .	−1.20	−0.96	27.53	27.95	57.53	58.13	−993.71 ± 0.23	−993.91	−41.66 ± 0.25	−41.66
3-" . .	−0.54	−0.48	28.27	28.34	58.36	58.47	−994.25 ± 0.21	−994.38	−41.02 ± 0.23	−41.03
2,2-Dimethylbutane .	−2.37	−1.53	27.46	28.51	58.53	59.70	−991.52 ± 0.21	−991.97	−44.35 ± 0.23	−43.98
2,3-" .	−0.98	−0.77	28.51	28.69	59.28	59.36	−993.05 ± 0.22	−993.52	−42.49 ± 0.24	−42.18
n-Heptane . .	1.94	1.84	35.14	35.12	69.83	69.81	−1151.27 ± 0.15	−1151.40	−44.89 ± 0.19	−44.92
2-Methylhexane .	0.77	1.07	34.24	34.85	69.15	70.03	−1149.97 ± 0.28	−1150.14	−46.60 ± 0.30	−46.62
3-" . .	1.10	1.55	34.40	35.24	69.21	70.37	−1150.55 ± 0.28	−1150.61	−45.96 ± 0.30	−45.99
3-Ethylpentane .	2.57	2.03	36.41	35.62	71.94	70.71	−1151.13 ± 0.26	−1151.08	−45.34 ± 0.28	−45.36

*Equations for calculation (49):

$$\Delta Z°(el., gas) = \sum_{i \leqslant j=1}^{4} n_{ij} Z_{ij}(el., gas) - \sum_{i \leqslant j=1}^{4} n_{ij} H_{ij}(comb., liq.); \quad \Delta H°(comb., liq.); \quad \Delta H°(el., gas) = \sum_{i \leqslant j=1}^{4} n_{ij} H_{ij}(el., gas)$$

constants H_{ij}(comb., liq.) and H_{ij}(el., gas) being taken from Table 9, constants Z_{ij} (el., gas) from Table 10.

H

TABLE 18 (contd.)

Hydrocarbon	T = 298.16° K ΔZ° (el., r. gas) exp. from [50]	calc. from eq. (4g)*	T = 500° K ΔZ° (el., r. gas) exp. from [50]	calc. from eq. (4g)*	T = 700° K exp. from [50]	calc. from eq. (4g)*	T = 298.16° K ΔH (comb., liq.) exp. from [50]	calc. from eq. (4g)*	T = 298.16° K ΔH (el., gas) exp. from [50]	calc. from eq (4g)*
2,2-Dimethylpentane	0.02	0.50	34.81	35.40	71.19	71.61	−1147.85 ±0.30	−1148.20	−49.29 ±0.30	−48.94
2,3- "	0.16	1.74	33.90	35.98	69.24	71.60	−1149.09 ±0.28	−1150.22	−47.62 ±0.30	−46.51
2,4- "	0.72	0.29	35.28	34.58	71.37	70.26	−1148.73 ±0.20	−1148.88	−48.30 ±0.23	−48.32
3,3- "	0.63	1.29	35.02	35.92	70.92	71.97	−1148.83 ±0.19	−1149.23	−48.17 ±0.22	−47.84
2,2,3-Trimethylbutane	1.02	1.36	36.38	36.58	73.11	73.12	−1148.27 ±0.25	−1148.93	−48.96 ±0.27	−48.53
n-Octane	3.95	3.87	42.02	42.01	81.74	81.71	−1307.53 ±0.16	−1307.63	−49.82 ±0.20	−49.88
2-Methylheptane	3.06	3.09	41.58	41.74	81.63	81.94	−1306.92 ±0.28	−1306.37	−51.50 ±0.31	−51.58
3- "	3.29	3.58	41.50	42.13	81.31	82.28	−1307.09 ±0.25	−1306.84	−50.84 ±0.27	−50.95
4- "	4.00	3.58	41.62	42.13	82.88	82.88	−1307.39 ±0.23	−1307.31	−50.69 ±0.28	−50.95
3-Ethylhexane	3.95	4.06	42.39	42.52	82.64	82.62			−50.40 ±0.26	−50.32
2,2-Dimethylhexane	2.56	2.52	42.20	42.29	83.48	83.51	−1304.64 ±0.21	−1304.43	−53.71 ±0.24	−53.90
2,3- "	4.23	3.76	43.16	42.87	83.64	83.50	−1306.86 ±0.34	−1306.45	−51.13 ±0.36	−51.47
2,4- "	2.80	2.80	41.72	41.86	82.32	82.50	−1305.80 ±0.24	−1305.58	−52.44 ±0.27	−52.65
2,5- "	2.50	2.32	41.75	41.47	82.69	82.16	−1305.00 ±0.34	−1305.11	−53.21 ±0.36	−53.28
3,3- "	3.17	3.31	42.50	42.81	83.47	83.87	−1305.68 ±0.23	−1305.46	−52.61 ±0.26	−52.80
3,4- "	4.14	4.24	43.08	43.26	83.54	83.84	−1307.04 ±0.35	−1306.92	−50.91 ±0.37	−50.84
2-Methyl-3-ethylpentane	5.08	4.24	44.24	43.26	84.96	83.84	−1307.58 ±0.28	−1306.92	−50.48 ±0.31	−50.84
3-Methyl-3- "	4.76	4.10	44.30	43.33	85.48	84.23	−1306.80 ±0.27	−1306.48	−51.38 ±0.30	−51.70
2,2,3-Trimethylpentane	4.09	3.86	43.98	43.86	85.54	85.36	−1305.83 ±0.34	−1305.63	−52.61 ±0.36	−52.86

*Equations for calculation (4g):

$$\Delta Z°(el.,gas)=\sum_{i\leqslant j=1}^{4} n_{ij}Z_{ij}(el.,gas); \quad \Delta H°(comb.,liq.)=\sum_{i\leqslant j=1}^{4} n_{ij}H_{ij}(comb.,liq.); \quad \Delta H°(el.,gas)=\sum_{i\leqslant j=1}^{4} n_{ij}H_{ij}(el.,gas);$$

constants H_{ij}(comb.,liq.) and H_{ij}(el.,gas) being taken from Table 9; constants Z_{ij}(el., gas) from Table 10.

TABLE 18 (contd.)

Hydrocarbon	T = 298.16° K ΔZ° (el., gas)		T = 500° K		T = 700° K	T = 298.16° K ΔH (comb., liq.)		T = 298.16° K ΔH (el., gas)	
	experimental from [50]	calculated from eq. (4g)*	experimental from [50]	calculated from eq. (4g)*	calculated from eq. (4g)*	experimental from [50]	calculated from eq. (4g)*	experimental from [50]	calculated from eq. (4g)*
2,2,4-Trimethylpentane	3.27	1.75	43.28	42.02	83.74	−1305.29 ± 0.30	−1303.17	−53.57 ± 0.32	−55.60
2,3,3- "	4.52	4.17	44.08	43.99	85.38	−1306.64 ± 0.31	−1306.18	−51.73 ± 0.33	−52.39
2,3,4- "	4.52	3.95	44.24	43.61	84.73	−1306.28 ± 0.38	−1306.07	−51.97 ± 0.40	−51.99
2,2,3,3-Tetramethylbutane	5.27	(5.27)	48.90	(48.90)	(93.65)	−	−	−53.99 ± 0.46	−53.99
n-Nonane	5.96	5.90	48.90	48.90	93.62	−1463.80 ± 0.18	−1463.86	−54.74 ± 0.22	−54.84
2-Methyloctane	—	5.14	—	48.61	93.83	—	−1462.60	—	−56.54
3- "	—	5.62	—	49.00	94.17	—	−1463.07	—	−55.91
4- "	—	5.62	—	49.00	94.17	—	−1463.07	—	−55.91
3-Ethylheptane	—	6.10	—	49.39	94.51	—	−1463.54	—	−55.28
4- "	—	6.10	—	49.39	94.51	—	−1463.54	—	−55.28
2,2-Dimethylheptane	—	4.55	—	49.16	95.41	—	−1460.66	—	−58.86
2,3- "	—	5.80	—	49.74	95.41	—	−1462.68	—	−56.43
2,4- "	—	4.84	—	48.73	94.40	—	−1461.81	—	−57.61
2,5- "	—	4.84	—	48.73	94.40	—	−1461.81	—	−57.61
2,6- "	—	4.36	—	48.34	94.06	—	−1461.34	—	−58.24
3,3- "	—	5.34	—	49.68	95.78	—	−1461.69	—	−57.76
3,4- "	—	6.28	—	50.13	95.75	—	−1463.16	—	−55.80
3,5- "	—	5.32	—	49.12	94.74	—	−1462.28	—	−56.98
4,4- "	—	5.34	—	49.68	95.78	—	−1461.69	—	−57.76

*Equations for calculation (4g):

$$\Delta z°(\text{el., gas}) = \sum_{i<j=1}^{4} n_{ij}Z_{ij}(\text{el., gas}); \quad \Delta H°(\text{comb., liq.}) = \sum_{i<j=1}^{4} n_{ij}H_{ij}(\text{comb., liq.}); \quad \Delta H°(\text{el., gas}) = \sum_{i<j=1}^{4} n_{ij}H_{ij}(\text{el., gas});$$

$$\Delta H°(\text{comb., liq.}) - \Delta H°(\text{el., gas}) = \sum_{i<j=1}^{4} n_{ij}H_{ij}(\text{el., gas});$$

constants H_{ij} (comb., liq.) and H_{ij} (el., gas) being taken from Table 9; constants Z_{ij} (el., gas) from Table 10.

TABLE 18 (contd.)

Hydrocarbon	$T = 298.16°$ K ΔZ° (el., gas) experimental from [50]	$T = 298.16°$ K ΔZ° (el., gas) calculated from eq.(4g)*	$T = 500°$ K (el., gas) experimental from [50]	$T = 500°$ K (el., gas) calculated from eq.(4g)*	$T = 700°$ K experimental from [50]	$T = 700°$ K calculated from eq.(4g)*	$T = 298.16°$ K ΔH (comb., liq.) experimental from [50]	$T = 298.16°$ K ΔH (comb., liq.) calculated from eq.(4g)*	$T = 298.16°$ K ΔH (el., gas) experimental from [50]	$T = 298.16°$ K ΔH (el., gas) calculated from eq.(4g)*
2-Methyl-3-ethylhexane . .	—	6.28	—	50.13	—	95.75	—	−1463.15	—	−55.80
3-Methyl-3- " . .	—	6.13	—	50.20	—	96.15	—	−1462.71	—	−53.66
2-Methyl-4- " . .	—	5.32	—	49.12	—	94.74	—	−1462.28	—	−56.98
3-Methyl-4- " . .	—	6.76	!	50.52	—	96.09	—	−1463.62	—	−55.17
2,2,3-Trimethylhexane . .	—	5.89	—	50.73	—	97.26	—	−1461.86	—	−57.82
2,2,4- " . .	—	4.25	—	49.28	—	95.98	—	−1459.87	—	−59.93
2,2,5- " . .	—	3.77	—	48.89	—	95.64	—	−1459.40	—	−60.56
2,3,3- " . .	—	6.20	—	50.86	—	97.29	—	−1462.41	—	−57.35
2,3,4- " . .	—	6.46	—	50.87	—	96.99	—	−1462.77	—	−56.32
2,3,5- " . .	—	5.02	—	49.47	—	95.64	—	−1461.42	—	−58.12
3,3,4- " . .	—	6.68	—	51.25	—	97.63	—	−1462.88	—	−56.72
3,3,5- " . .	—	4.56	—	49.41	—	96.01	—	−1460.43	—	−59.46
3,3-Diethylpentane . . .	—	6.92	—	50.72	—	96.52	−1463.79 ± 0.38	−1463.74	—	−55.56
2,2-Dimethyl-3-ethylpentane	—	6.37	—	51.12	—	97.60	—	−1462.33	—	−57.19
2,3-Dimethyl-3- "	—	6.99	—	51.38	—	97.66	—	−1463.44	—	−56.25
2,4-Dimethyl-3- "	—	6.46	—	50.87	—	96.99	—	−1462.77	—	−56.32
2,2,3,3-Tetramethylpentane	—	7.99	—	54.35	—	102.22	−1463.10 ± 0.36	—	—	−57.85
2,2,3,4- "	—	6.07	—	51.47	—	98.50	−1463.24 ± 0.28	−1461.47	—	−58.34
2,2,4,4- "	—	3.18	—	49.44	—	97.22	−1462.69 ± 0.31	−1457.47	—	−62.88
2,3,3,4- "	—	7.06	—	52.04	—	98.80	−1463.18 ± 0.39	−1463.14	—	−56.94

*Equations for calculation (4g):

$$\Delta Z°(\text{el.,gas}) = \sum_{i \leqslant j=1}^{4} n_{ij} Z_{ij}(\text{el.,gas}); \quad \Delta H°(\text{comb.,liq.}) = \sum_{i \leqslant j=1}^{4} n_{ij} H_{ij}(\text{comb.,liq.}); \quad \Delta H°(\text{el.,gas}) = \sum_{i \leqslant j=1}^{4} n_{ij} H_{ij}(\text{el.,gas});$$

constants H_{ij} (comb.,liq.) and H_{ij} (el.,gas) being taken from Table 9; constants Z_{ij} (el.,gas) from Table 10.

TABLE 18 (contd.)

Hydrocarbon	$T = 298,16°$ K $\Delta Z°$ (el.,gas) experimental from [50]	$T = 298,16°$ K $\Delta Z°$ (el.,gas) calculated from eq. (4g)*	$T = 500°$ K $\Delta Z°$ (el.,gas) experimental from [50]	$T = 500°$ K $\Delta Z°$ (el.,gas) calculated from eq. (4g)*	$T = 700°$ K experimental from [50]	$T = 700°$ K calculated from eq. (4g)*	$T = 298,16°$ K ΔH (comb.,liq.) experimental from [50]	$T = 298,16°$ K ΔH (comb.,liq.) calculated from eq. (4g)*	$T = 298,16°$ K ΔH (el.,gas) experimental from [50]	$T = 298,16°$ K ΔH (el.,gas) calculated from eq. (4g)*
n-Decane	—	7.92	—	55.79	—	105.52	—	—1620.09	—	—59.80
2-Methylnonane	—	7.17	—	55.50	—	105.73	—	—1618.82	—	—61.50
3- =	—	7.65	—	55.89	—	106.07	—	—1619.29	—	—60.87
4- =	—	7.65	—	55.89	—	106.07	—	—1619.29	—	—60.87
5- =	—	7.65	—	55.89	—	106.07	—	—1619.29	—	—60.87
3-Ethyloctane	—	8.13	—	56.28	—	106.41	—	—1619.76	—	—60.24
4- =	—	8.13	—	56.28	—	106.41	—	—1619.76	—	—60.24
2,2-Dimethyloctane	—	6.58	—	56.05	—	107.31	—	—1616.90	—	—63.82
2,3- =	—	7.83	—	56.63	—	107.31	—	—1618.90	—	—61.39
2,4- =	—	6.87	—	55.62	—	106.30	—	—1618.02	—	—62.57
2,5- =	—	6.87	—	55.62	—	106.30	—	—1618.02	—	—62.57
2,6- =	—	6.87	—	55.62	—	106.30	—	—1618.02	—	—62.57
2,7- =	—	6.39	—	55.23	—	105.96	—	—1617.55	—	—63.20
3,4- =	—	7.37	—	56.57	—	107.68	—	—1617.93	—	—62.72
3,5- =	—	8.31	—	57.02	—	107.65	—	—1619.37	—	—60.76
3,6- =	—	7.35	—	56.01	—	106.64	—	—1618.49	—	—61.94
4,4- =	—	7.37	—	56.57	—	107.68	—	—1617.93	—	—62.72
4,5- =	—	8.31	—	57.02	—	107.65	—	—1619.37	—	—60.76

*Equations for calculation (4g):

$$\Delta Z°(el.,gas) = \sum_{i \leqslant j=1}^{4} n_{ij} Z_{ij}(el.,gas); \quad \Delta H°(comb.,liq.) = \sum_{i \leqslant j=1}^{4} n_{ij} H_{ij}(comb.,liq.); \quad \Delta H°(el.,gas) = \sum_{i \leqslant j=1}^{4} n_{ij} H_{ij}(el.,gas);$$

constants $H_{ij}(comb.,liq.)$ and $H_{ij}(el.,gas)$ being taken from Table 9; constants $Z_{ij}(el.,gas)$ from Table 10.

TABLE 18 (contd.)

Hydrocarbon	T = 298.16°K ΔZ° (el., gas)		T = 500°K ΔZ° (el., gas)		T = 700°K ΔZ° (el., gas)		T = 298.16°K ΔH(comb., liq.)		T = 298.16°K ΔH(el., gas)	
	experimental from [50]	calculated from eq. (4g)*	experimental from [50]	calculated from eq. (4g)*	experimental from [50]	calculated from eq. (4g)*	experimental from [50]	calculated from eq. (4g)*	experimental from [50]	calculated from eq. (4g)*
2-Methyl-3-ethylheptane	—	8.31	—	57.02	—	107.65	—	—1619.37	—	—60.76
2-Methyl-4- "	—	7.35	—	56.01	—	106.64	—	—1618.49	—	—61.94
2-Methyl-5- "	—	7.35	—	56.01	—	106.64	—	—1618.49	—	—61.94
3-Methyl-3- "	—	8.16	—	57.09	—	108.05	—	—1618.96	—	—61.62
3-Methyl-4- "	—	8.79	—	57.41	—	107.99	—	—1619.84	—	—60.13
3-Methyl-5- "	—	7.83	—	56.40	—	106.98	—	—1618.96	—	—61.34
4-Methyl-5- "	—	8.79	—	57.41	—	107.99	—	—1619.84	—	—60.13
4-Methyl-4- "	—	8.16	—	57.09	—	108.05	—	—1618.96	—	—61.62
4-Propylheptane	—	8.13	—	56.28	—	106.41	—	—1619.76	—	—60.24
4-Isopropylheptane	—	8.31	—	57.02	—	107.65	—	—1619.37	—	—60.76
2,2,3-Trimethylheptane	—	7.92	—	57.62	—	109.16	—	—1618.08	—	—62.78
2,2,4- "	—	6.28	—	56.17	—	107.88	—	—1616.10	—	—64.89
2,2,5- "	—	5.80	—	55.78	—	107.54	—	—1616.10	—	—64.89
2,2,6- "	—	8.23	—	57.75	—	109.19	—	—1615.63	—	—65.52
2,3,3- "	—	8.49	—	57.76	—	108.89	—	—1618.64	—	—62.31
2,3,4- "	—	7.53	—	56.75	—	107.88	—	—1618.98	—	—61.28
2,3,5- "	—	7.05	—	56.36	—	107.54	—	—1618.10	—	—62.46
2,3,6- "	—	6.59	—	56.30	—	107.91	—	—1617.63	—	—63.09
2,4,4- "	—		—		—		—	—1616.66	—	—64.42

*Equations for calculation (4g):

$$\Delta Z° (el., gas) = \sum_{i<j=1}^{4} n_{ij} Z_{ij} (el., gas); \quad \Lambda H°(comb., liq.) = \sum_{i<j=1}^{4} n_{ij} H_{ij} (comb., liq.); \quad \Delta H°(el., gas) = \sum_{i<j=1}^{4} n_{ij} H_{ij} (el., gas);$$

constants H_{ij}(comb., liq.) and H_{ij}(el., gas) being taken from Table 9; constants Z_{ij}(el., gas) from Table 10.

TABLE 18 (contd.)

Hydrocarbon	$T = 298.16°$ K ΔZ°(el.,gas) experimental from [50]	$T = 298.16°$ K ΔZ°(el.,gas) calculated from eq.(4g)*	$T = 500°$ K ΔZ°(el.,gas) experimental from [50]	$T = 500°$ K ΔZ°(el.,gas) calculated from eq.(4g)*	$T = 700°$ K ΔZ°(el.,gas) experimental from [50]	$T = 700°$ K ΔZ°(el.,gas) calculated from eq.(4g)*	$T = 298.16°$ K ΔH(comb.,liq.) experimental from [50]	$T = 298.16°$ K ΔH(comb.,liq.) calculated from eq.(4g)	$T = 298.16°$ K ΔH(el.,gas) experimental from [50]	$T = 298.16°$ K ΔH(el.,gas) calculated from eq.(4g)*
2,4,5-Trimethylheptane	—	7.53	—	56.75	—	107.88	—	—1618.10	—	—62.46
2,4,6- "	—	6.09	—	55.35	—	106.53	—	—1616.75	—	—64.27
3,3,4- "	—	8.71	—	58.14	—	109.53	—	—1619.11	—	—61.68
3,3,5- "	—	7.07	—	56.69	—	108.25	—	—1617.13	—	—63.79
3,3,6- "	—	6.59	—	56.30	—	107.91	—	—1616.66	—	—64.42
3,4,4- "	—	8.71	—	58.14	—	109.53	—	—1619.11	—	—61.68
3,4,5- "	—	8.97	—	58.15	—	109.23	—	—1619.45	—	—60.65
3,3-Diethylhexane	—	8.95	—	57.61	—	108.42	—	—1619.99	—	—60.52
3,4- "	—	9.27	—	57.80	—	108.33	—	—1620.31	—	—59.50
2,2-Dimethyl-3-ethylhexane	—	8.40	—	58.01	—	109.50	—	—1618.55	—	—62.15
2,2-Dimethyl-4- "	—	6.76	—	56.56	—	108.22	—	—1616.57	—	—64.26
2,3-Dimethyl-3- "	—	9.02	—	58.27	—	109.56	—	—1619.67	—	—61.21
2,3-Dimethyl-4- "	—	8.97	—	58.15	—	109.23	—	—1619.45	—	—60.65
2,4-Dimethyl-3- "	—	8.97	—	58.15	—	109.23	—	—1619.45	—	—60.65
2,4-Dimethyl-4- "	—	7.38	—	56.82	—	108.28	—	—1617.69	—	—63.32
2,5-Dimethyl-3- "	—	7.53	—	56.75	—	107.88	—	—1618.10	—	—62.46
3,3-Dimethyl-4- "	—	9.19	—	58.53	—	109.87	—	—1619.58	—	—61.05
3,4-Dimethyl-4- "	—	9.50	—	58.66	—	109.90	—	—1620.14	—	—60.58
2-Methyl-3-isopropylhexane	—	8.49	—	57.76	—	108.89	—	—1618.98	—	—61.28

*Equations for calculation (4g):

$$\Delta Z°(\text{el.,gas}) = \sum_{i \leqslant j = 1}^{4} n_{ij} Z_{ij}(\text{el.,gas}); \quad \Delta H°(\text{comb.,liq.}) = \sum_{i \leqslant j = 1}^{4} n_{ij} H_{ij}(\text{comb.,liq.}); \quad \Delta H°(\text{el.,gas}) = \sum_{i \leqslant j = 1}^{4} n_{ij} H_{ij}(\text{el.,gas});$$

constants H_{ij} (comb.,liq.) and H_{ij} (el.,gas) being taken from Table 9; constants Z_{ij} (el.,gas) from Table 10.

TABLE 18 (contd.)

Hydrocarbon	$T = 298.16°\,K$ $\Delta Z°$(el.,gas) experimental from [50]	$T = 298.16°\,K$ $\Delta Z°$(el.,gas) calculated from eq. (4g)*	$T = 500°\,K$ $\Delta Z°$(el.,gas) experimental from [50]	$T = 500°\,K$ $\Delta Z°$(el.,gas) calculated from eq. (4g)*	$T = 700°\,K$ $\Delta Z°$(el.,gas) experimental from [50]	$T = 700°\,K$ $\Delta Z°$(el.,gas) calculated from eq. (4g)*	$T = 298.16°\,K$ ΔH(comb.,liq.) experimental from [50]	$T = 298.16°\,K$ ΔH(comb.,liq.) calculated from eq. (4g)*	$T = 298.16°\,K$ ΔH(el.,gas) experimental from [50]	$T = 298.16°\,K$ ΔH(el.,gas) calculated from eq. (4g)*
2,2,3,3-Tetramethylhexane	—	10.02	—	61.24	—	114.12	—	−1618.16	—	−62.81
2,3,4— =	—	8.58	—	58.75	—	110.74	—	−1616.81	—	−62.67
2,3,5— =	—	7.14	—	57.35	—	109.39	—	−1614.74	—	−64.48
2,2,4,4— =	—	6.06	—	56.85	—	109.49	—	−1615.71	—	−66.74
2,2,4,5— =	—	6.46	—	56.91	—	109.12	—	−1613.71	—	−65.41
2,2,5,5— =	—	5.21	—	56.33	—	109.12	—	—	—	−67.84
2,3,3,4— =	—	9.57	—	59.32	—	111.04	—	−1619.82	—	−61.27
2,3,3,5— =	—	7.45	—	57.48	—	109.42	—	−1617.37	—	−64.01
2,3,4,5— =	—	8.67	—	58.50	—	110.13	—	−1618.59	—	−61.80
3,3,4,5— =	—	10.81	—	61.76	—	114.49	—	—	—	−61.71
2,2,3—Trimethyl-3—ethylpentane	—	8.89	—	58.88	—	110.77	—	−1618.72	—	−62.20
2,2,4—Trimethyl-3— "	—	10.81	—	61.76	—	114.49	—	—	—	−61.71
2,3,4—Trimethyl-3— "	—	8.58	—	58.75	—	110.74	—	−1618.16	—	−62.67
2,4—Dimethyl-3—isopropyl-pentane	—	9.88	—	59.45	—	111.07	—	−1620.38	—	−60.80
3,3—Diethyl-4—methylpentane	—	8.67	—	58.50	—	110.13	—	−1618.59	—	−61.80
2,2,3,3,4—Pentamethylpentane	—	9.81	—	58.79	—	109.93	—	−1620.70	—	−60.11
2,2,3,4,4—Pentamethylpentane	—	10.88	—	62.42	—	115.63	—	—	—	−63.40
2,2,3,4,4— "	—	8.19	—	59.35	—	112.25	—	−1616.87	—	−64.69

*Equations for calculation (4g):

$$\Delta Z°(\text{el.,gas}) = \sum_{i\leqslant j=1}^{4} n_{ij} Z_{ij}(\text{el.,gas}); \qquad \Delta H°(\text{comb.,liq.}) = \sum_{i\leqslant j=1}^{4} n_{ij} H_{ij}(\text{comb.,liq.}); \qquad \Delta H°(\text{el.,gas}) = \sum_{i\leqslant j=1}^{4} n_{ij} H_{ij}(\text{el.,gas});$$

constants H_{ij}(comb.,liq.) and H_{ij}(el.,gas) being taken from Table 9; constants Z_{ij}(el.,gas) from Table 10.

TABLE 19

Experimental and calculated* values of the boiling point of alkanes

Hydrocarbon	t_{boil} °C		Error in calcula-tion, °C
	experimental from [50]	calculated from eq. (21)	
n-Hexane	68.7	70.4	—1.7
2-Methylpentane	60.3	60.7	—0.4
3- "	63.3	62.5	+0.8
2,2-Dimethylbutane	49.7	49.3	+0.4
2,3- "	58.0	57.5	+0.5
n-Heptane	98.4	98.0	+0.4
2-Methylhexane	90.1	90.2	—0.1
3- "	91.9	91.0	+0.9
2,2-Dimethylpentane	79.2	80.4	—1.2
2,3- "	89.8	88.4	+1.4
2,4- "	80.5	81.1	—0.6
3,3- "	86.1	83.9	+2.2
3-Ethylpentane	93.5	92.0	+1.5
2,2,3-Trimethylbutane	80.9	80.3	+0.6
n-Octane	125.7	125.4	+0.3
2-Methylheptane	117.6	117.2	+0.4
3- "	118.9	118.2	+0.7
4- "	117.7	118.2	—0.5
3-Ethylhexane	118.5	118.9	—0.4
2,2-Dimethylhexane	106.8	108.9	—2.1
2,3- "	115.6	115.8	—0.2
2,4- "	109.4	109.9	—0.5

*Equation for calculation (21):

$$t_{boil} = \frac{\sum_{i \leqslant j = 1}^{4} n_{ij} \lambda_{ij}}{\sum_{i \leqslant j = 1}^{4} n_{ij} b_{ij} - \log p} ;$$

constants λ_{ij} being taken from Table 5, b_{ij} from Table 6.

TABLE 19 (contd.)

Hydrocarbon	t_{boil} °C experimental from [50]	t_{boil} °C calculated from eq. (21)	Error in calculation, °C
2,5-Dimethylhexane	109.1	108.9	+0.2
3,3- "	112.0	112.6	−0.6
3,4- "	117.7	116.9	+0.8
2-Methyl-3-ethylpentane	115.7	116.9	−1.2
3-Methyl-3- "	118.3	116.4	+1.9
2,2,3-Trimethylpentane	109.8	110.3	−0.5
2,2,4- "	99.2	100.1	−0.9
2,3,3- "	114.8	113.2	+1.6
2,3,4- "	113.5	113.6	−0.1
n-Nonane	150.8	150.9	−0.1
2-Methyloctane	143.3	143.3	0.0
3- "	144.2	144.0	+0.2
4- "	142.5	144.0	−1.5
3-Ethylheptane	143.1	143.6	−0.5
4- "	142.2 .	143.6	−1.4
	141.2		−2.4
2,2-Dimethylheptane	132.7	134.8	−2.1
2,3- "	140.7	141.2	−0.5
2,4- "	133.5	135.2	−1.7
2,5- "	136.0	135.2	+0.8
2,6- "	135.2	135.6	−0.4
3,3- "	137.3	136.5	−0.8
	137.0		−0.5
3,4- "	140.1	140.8	−0.7
	140.6		−0.2
3,5- "	136.0	136.9	−0.9
4,4- "	135.2	136.5	−1.3
	134.4		−2.1
2-Methyl-3-ethylhexane	138.0	140.8	−2.8
3-Methyl-3- "	—	143.2	—
2-Methyl-4- "	—	136.9	—

TABLE 19 (contd.)

| Hydrocarbon | t_{boil} °C | | Error in calcula- tion, °C |
	experimental from [50]	calculated from eq. (21)	
3-Methyl-4-ethylhexane	141.9	142.4	—0.5
2,2,3-Trimethylhexane	135.0	135.9	—0.9
	133.6		—2.3
2,2,4- "	126.5	127.0	—0.5
2,2,5- "	124.1	125.1	—1.0
2,3,3- "	137.7	138.0	—0.3
2,3,4- "	139.0	138.9	+0.1
2,3,5- "	131.4	133.2	—1.8
2,4,4- "	130.6	131.2	—0.6
3,3,4- "	140.4	140.9	—0.5
3,3,5- "	130.6	131.2	—0.6
3,3-Diethylpentane	146.2	147.1	—0.9
2,2-Dimethyl-3-ethylpentane . . .	133.8	135.5	—1.7
2,3-Dimethyl-3- " . . .	141.6	144.3	—2.7
2,4-Dimethyl-3- " . . .	136.7	138.8	—2.1
2,2,3,4-Tetramethylpentane . . .	133.0	134.7	—1.7
2,2,4,4- " . . .	122.3	118.8	+3.5
2,3,3,4- " . . .	141.6	141.3	+0.3
n-Decane	174.1	174.8	+0.7
2-Methylnonane	167.0	167.9	+0.9
3- "	167.8	168.6	+0.8
4- "	165.7	168.6	+2.9
5- "	165.1	168.6	+3.5
3-Ethyloctane	(168.0)	169.0	+1.0
4- "	(168.0)	169.0	+1.0
2,2-Dimethyloctane	(155.3)	160.8	+5.5
2,3- "	164.3	167.6	+3.3
2,4- "	(153.0)	161.4	+8.4
2,5- "	158.4	161.4	+3.0
2,6- "	158.5	161.4	+3.0
2,7- "	159.9	160.8	+0.9
3,3- "	161.2	164.6	+3.4
3,4- "	(166.0)	167.4	+1.4

TABLE 19 (contd.)

Hydrocarbon	t_{boil} °C		Error in calculation, °C
	experimental from [50]	calculated from eq. (21)	
3,5–Dimethyloctane	(160.0)	162.2	+2.2
3,6– "	(160.0)	162.2	+2.2
4,4– "	(161.0)	164.6	+3.6
4,5– "	162.1	167.4	+5.2
2–Methyl–3–ethylheptane	(166)	167.4	+1.4
2–Methyl–4– "	(160)	162.2	+2.2
2–Methyl–5– "	159.7	162.2	+2.5
3–Methyl–3– "	163.8	168.5	+4.7
3–Methyl–4– "	(167)	167.4	+0.4
3–Methyl–5– "	(161)	162.8	+1.8
4–Methyl–3– "	167	167.0	0.0
4–Methyl–4– "	(167)	168.5	+1.5
4–Propylheptane	162.0	168.4	+6.4
4–Isopropylheptane	(168)	165.4	−2.6
2,2,3–Trimethylheptane	(158)	164.2	+6.2
2,2,4– "	149.4	154.0	+4.6
2,2,5– "	(148)	154.0	+6.0
2,2,6– "	148.9	153.3	+4.4
2,3,3– "	(160)	164.0	+4.0
2,3,4– "	163.4	164	+1.4
2,3,5– "	157	159.4	+2.4
2,3,6– "	155.7	158.6	+2.9
2,4,4– "	153	157.3	+4.3
2,4,5– "	157	159.4	+2.4
2,4,6– "	147.6	152.4	+4.8
2,5,5– "	158.8	161.5	+2.7
3,3,4– "	164	166.5	+2.5
3,3,5– "	155.7	158.8	+3.1
3,4,4– "	164	161.5	−2.5
3,4,5– "	164	164.8	+0.8
3,3–Diethylhexane	166.3	172.3	+6.0
3,4– "	169	168.0	−1.0
2,2–Dimethyl–3–ethylhexane	159	163.3	+4.3

TABLE 19 (contd.)

Hydrocarbon	t_{boil} °C		Error in calcula-tion, °C
	experimental from [50]	calculated from eq. (21)	
2,2-Dimethyl-4-ethylhexane	147	154.6	+7.6
2,3-Dimethyl-3- "	169	169.7	+0.7
2,3-Dimethyl-4- "	164	164.8	+0.8
2,4-Dimethyl-3- "	164	164.8	+0.8
2,4-Dimethyl-4- "	158	161.2	+3.2
2,5-Dimethyl-3- "	157	159.4	+2.4
3,3-Dimethyl-4- "	165	167.2	+2.2
3,4-Dimethyl-4- "	170	170.4	+0.4
2-Methyl-3-isopropylhexane	163	164.2	+1.2
2,2,3,3-Tetramethylhexane	160	—	—
2,2,3,4- "	154.9	160.6	+5.7
2,2,3,5- "	148.4	155.2	+6.8
2,2,4,4- "	153.3	149.6	—3.7
2,2,4,5- "	147.9	151.3	+3.4
2,2,5,5- "	137.5	145.6	+8.1
2,3,3,4- "	164.6	169.8	+5.2
2,3,3,5- "	153	170.4	+17.4
2,3,4,5- "	161	160.8	—0.2
3,3,4,4- "	170.0	—	—
3,3,4,5- "	162.2	163.9	+1.7
2,2,3-Trimethyl-3-ethylpentane . .	168	—	
2,2,4-Trimethyl-3-ethylpentane . .	155.3	160.6	+5.3
2,3,4-Trimethyl-3-ethylpentane . .	169.4	168.8	—0.6
2,4-Dimethyl-3-isopropylpentane . .	157.0	161.6	+4.6
3,3-Diethyl-2-methylpentane . . .	174	173.6	—0.4
2,2,3,3,4-Pentamethylpentane . . .	166.1	—	—
2,2,3,4,4- " . . .	159.3	156.2	—3.1
n-Undecane	195.9,	197.3	+1.4
n-Dodecane	216.3	218.5	+2.2
n-Tridecane	235.5	238.6	+3.1
n-Tetradecane	253.6	257.3	+3.7
n-Pentadecane	270.8	275.1	+4.3
n-Hexadecane	287.1	292.0	+4.9

TAB

Calculated values of certain phys

Distribution of bonds									$\Delta H_{298.16°K}$ (el., gas) kcal/mol	$\Delta H_{298.16°K}$ (comb., liq) kcal/mol	$\Delta H_{298.16°K}$ (comb., gas) kcal/mol	$\Delta Z_{298.16°K}$, kcal/mol	R_N^{20}, ml/mol
n_{12}	n_{13}	n_{14}	n_{22}	n_{23}	n_{24}	n_{33}	n_{34}	n_{44}					
4	0	0	1	4	0	1	0	0	64.46	1776.54	1789.95	11.30	52.464
2	4	0	0	0	2	0	2	0	64.66	1777.64	1789.76	12.70	51.998
2	0	0	8	0	0	0	0	0	64.76	1776.32	1789.62	9.98	53.134
3	1	0	2	3	0	1	0	0	65.09	1776.07	1789.32	10.82	52.611
2	3	1	0	1	1	0	2	0	65.13	1777.08	1789.29	12.39	52.105
3	0	0	4	3	0	0	0	0	65.20	1775.99	1789.20	10.16	52.876
0	6	1	0	0	0	0	3	0	65.35	1777.32	1789.09	12.77	52.048
4	0	0	2	0	4	0	0	0	65.48	1776.22	1788.90	10.98	52.406
3	1	1	1	1	2	0	1	0	65.54	1776.37	1788.86	11.53	52.309
3	0	3	0	0	3	0	0	1	65.57	1777.63	1788.81	13.63	52.007
2	2	2	0	2	0	0	2	0	65.60	1776.52	1788.82	12.08	52.212
2	2	0	3	2	0	1	0	0	65.72	1775.60	1788.69	10.34	52.758
1	4	1	1	0	1	0	2	0	65.76	1776.61	1788.66	11.91	52.252
2	1	0	5	2	0	0	0	0	65.83	1775.52	1788.57	9.68	53.027
3	0	2	1	2	1	0	1	0	66.01	1775.81	1788.39	11.20	52.416
2	3	1	0	0	2	1	1	0	66.06	1775.98	1788.35	11.71	52.191
1	5	0	0	1	0	3	0	0	66.13	1775.29	1788.30	11.18	52.375
2	2	1	2	0	2	0	1	0	66.17	1775.90	1788.25	11.03	52.456
1	3	2	1	1	0	0	2	0	66.23	1776.05	1788.19	11.60	52.359
1	2	4	0	0	1	0	1	1	66.26	1777.31	1788.14	13.70	52.057
3	1	0	1	5	0	0	0	0	66.27	1775.19	1788.15	9.86	52.767
1	3	0	4	1	0	1	0	0	66.35	1775.13	1788.06	9.86	52.905
1	2	0	6	1	0	0	0	0	66.46	1775.05	1787.94	9.20	53.170
2	2	2	0	1	1	1	1	0	66.53	1775.44	1787.88	11.40	52.298
3	0	1	3	0	3	0	0	0	66.58	1775.19	1787.80	10.19	52.660
2	1	2	2	1	1	0	1	0	66.64	1775.34	1787.76	10.74	52.563
2	0	4	1	0	2	0	0	1	66.67	1776.60	1787.71	12.84	52.261
4	0	0	6	0	0	0	0	0	65.64	1775.66	1788.78	10.34	52.620
3	2	0	0	3	0	2	0	0	64.98	1776.15	1789.42	11.48	52.346
2	3	0	1	2	0	2	0	0	65.61	1775.68	1788.79	11.00	52.493
1	4	0	2	1	0	2	0	0	66.24	1775.21	1788.16	10.52	52.670
0	6	0	0	2	0	2	0	0	67.94	1773.94	1786.48	9.74	12.678
3	2	0	0	1	4	0	0	0	67.18	1774.95	1787.22	10.20	52.444
3	1	1	0	2	3	0	0	0	67.65	1774.39	1786.75	9.89	52.551
3	0	2	0	3	2	0	0	0	68.12	1773.83	1786.28	9.58	52.658
4	1	0	0	1	3	0	1	0	64.44	1777.40	1789.96	12.32	52.055
4	0	1	0	2	2	0	1	0	64.91	1776.84	1789.49	12.01	52.162
3	2	0	1	3	0	1	0	0	65.07	1776.93	1789.33	11.84	52.202
2	2	1	1	1	3	0	0	0	68.28	1773.92	1786.12	9.41	52.698
2	1	2	1	2	2	0	0	0	68.75	1773.36	1785.65	9.10	52.805
2	0	3	1	3	1	0	0	0	69.22	1772.80	1785.18	8.79	52.912

20

o-chemical properties of undecanes

$V_M^{20°}$, ml./mol	λ°, cal/mole					log p, mm mercury				
	40—80° C	70—110° C	90—130° C	110—150° C	130—170° C	60° C	90° C	110°C	130°C	150°C
202.450	2616.3	2524.3	2460.4	2401.2	2340.5	0.7594	1.4162	1.7671	2.0944	2.3881
195.618	2566.2	2438.4	2391.8	2347.6	2306.6	0.8222	1.4046	1.7420	2.0556	2.3176
210.960	2761.2	2628.4	2558.0	2495.6	2441.2	0.6354	1.3114	1.6820	2.0136	2.3010
204.501	2621.6	2521.1	2557.1	2398.8	2340.1	0.7738	1.4267	1.7798	2.1032	2.3953
197.080	2543.3	2431.2	2382.3	2335.0	2292.1	0.8683	1.4413	1.7762	2.0901	2.3538
207.861	2661.9	2555.3	2489.0	2429.2	2372.6	0.7434	1.4047	1.7620	2.0900	2.3717
195.967	2532.3	2408.2	2363.2	2319.4	2280.4	0.9215	1.4507	1.7841	2.0917	2.3488
201.904	2598.8	2478.0	2423.4	2374.0	2329.2	0.7446	1.4068	1.7516	2.0700	2.3418
200.223	2559.6	2451.0	2398.1	2348.2	2303.4	0.8295	1.4424	1.7810	2.0973	2.3660
194.724	—	—	—	—	—	—	—	—	—	—
198.542	2520.4	2424.0	2372.8	2322.4	2277.6	0.9144	1.4780	1.8104	2.1246	2.3902
206.510	2626.9	2517.9	2453.8	2396.4	2339.7	0.7882	1.4372	1.7925	2.1120	2.4025
199.110	2548.6	2428.0	2379.0	2332.6	2291.7	0.8827	1.4518	1.7889	2.0989	2.3610
209.891	2667.2	2552.1	2485.7	2426.8	2372.2	0.7578	1.4152	1.7747	2.09888	2.3789
201.685	2536.7	2443.8	2388.6	2335.6	2288.9	0.8743	1.4791	1.8152	2.1318	2.4024
198.872	2524.6	2413.6	2362.9	2315.4	2270.5	0.8756	1.4749	1.8115	2.1193	2.3968
201.778	2551.6	2446.3	2386.7	2333.2	2274.3	0.8634	1.4917	1.8408	2.1472	2.4569
202.253	2564.9	2447.8	2394.8	2345.8	2303.0	0.8439	1.4529	1.7937	2.1061	2.3732
200.572	2525.7	2420.8	2369.5	2320.0	2277.2	0.9288	1.4885	1.8231	2.1334	2.3974
207.697	—	—	—	—	—	—	—	—	—	—
206.792	2567.9	2479.0	2416.7	2360.4	2303.6	0.8658	1.5085	1.8547	2.1752	2.4496
208.540	2632.2	2514.7	2450.5	2394.0	2339.3	0.8026	1.4477	1.8052	2.1208	2.4097
211.921	2672.5	2548.9	2482.4	2424.4	2371.8	0.7722	1.4257	1.7874	2.1076	2.3861
200.334	2501.7	2406.4	2353.4	2302.8	2256.0	0.9204	1.5116	1.8457	2.1538	2.4332
205.396	2581.2	2467.6	2410.6	2359.0	2314.3	0.8051	1.4540	1.7985	2.1133	2.3856
203.715	2542.0	2440.6	2385.3	2333.2	2286.5	0.8900	1.4896	1.8279	2.1406	2.4049
198.216	—	—	—	—	—	—	—	—	—	—
204.762	2562.6	2482.2	2420.0	2362.8	2304.0	0.8514	1.4980	1.8420	2.1664	2.4424
201.099	2581.3	2486.9	2432.4	2368.4	2307.6	0.8042	1.4487	1.7976	2.1164	2.4189
203.129	2586.6	2483.7	2421.9	2366.0	2307.2	0.8186	1.4592	1.8103	2.1252	2.4261
205.159	2591.9	2480.5	2418.6	2363.6	2306.8	0.8330	1.4697	1.8230	2.1340	2.4333
206.120	2503.2	2401.0	2343.0	2292.4	2237.4	0.9698	1.5840	1.9284	2.2280	2.5184
201.862	2510.1	2398.5	2347.8	2302.8	2259.8	0.8814	1.5211	1.8570	2.1640	2.4269
204.327	2487.2	2391.3	2338.3	2290.2	2245.3	0.9275	1.5578	1.8912	2.1985	2.4633
205.789	2464.3	2384.1	2328.8	2277.6	2230.8	0.9736	1.5945	1.9254	2.2330	2.4997
209.355	2577.2	2461.4	2410.9	2363.2	2318.3	0.7690	1.3952	1.7341	2.0540	2.3224
198.193	2554.3	2454.2	2401.4	2350.6	2303.8	0.8151	1.4319	1.7683	2.0885	2.3590
198.761	2582.5	2458.2	2407.6	2260.8	2317.9	0.7834	1.4057	1.7468	2.0628	2.3296
206.357	2492.5	2388.1	2335.0	2287.8	2244.9	0.9419	1.5683	1.9039	2.2073	2.4705
207.819	2469.6	2380.9	2325.5	2275.2	2230.4	0.9880	1.6050	1.9381	2.2418	2.5069
209.281	2446.7	2373.7	2316.0	2262.6	2215.9	1.0341	1.6417	1.9723	2.2763	2.5433

TABLE 20 (contd.)

n_{12}	n_{13}	n_{14}	n_{22}	n_{23}	n_{24}	n_{33}	n_{34}	n_{44}	$\Delta H_{298.16°K}$ (el., gas) kcal/mol	$\Delta H_{298.16°K}$ (comb., liq.) kcal/mol	$\Delta H_{298.16°K}$ (ecomb., gas) kcal/mol	$\Delta Z_{298.16°K}$ kcal/mol	R_N^{20}, ml./mol
1	2	2	2	1	2	0	0	0	69.38	1772.89	1785.02	8.62	52.952
1	1	3	2	2	1	0	0	0	69.85	1772.33	1784.55	8.31	53.059
0	2	3	3	1	1	0	0	0	70.48	1771.86	1783.92	7.83	53.206
1	1	5	0	1	0	0	1	1	66.73	1776.75	1787.67	13.39	52.164
0	5	2	0	0	0	1	2	0	66.75	1775.66	1787.68	11.78	52.241
2	3	0	0	4	0	1	0	0	66.79	1774.80	1787.64	10.04	52.649
2	2	0	2	4	0	0	0	0	66.90	1774.72	1787.52	9.38	52.914
2	1	3	0	2	0	1	1	0	67.00	1774.86	1787.41	11.09	52.405
2	0	3	2	2	0	0	1	0	67.11	1774.78	1787.29	10.41	52.670
1	3	2	1	0	1	1	1	0	67.16	1774.95	1787.25	10.92	52.345
1	2	2	3	0	1	0	1	0	67.27	1774.87	1787.13	10.26	52.710
1	4	0	1	3	0	1	0	0	67.42	1774.33	1787.01	9.56	52.796
1	3	0	3	3	0	0	0	0	67.53	1774.25	1786.89	8.90	53.061
1	2	3	1	1	0	1	1	0	67.63	1774.39	1786.78	10.61	52.552
2	0	2	4	0	2	0	0	0	67.68	1774.16	1786.70	9.40	52.914
1	1	3	3	1	0	0	1	0	67.74	1774.31	1786.66	11.78	59.817
1	0	5	2	0	1	0	0	1	67.77	1775.57	1786.61	12.05	52.515
0	0	8	0	0	0	0	0	2	67.86	1776.98	1786.52	14.70	52.116
1	4	1	0	1	2	0	1	0	67.87	1774.63	1786.55	10.27	52.494
0	5	0	2	2	0	1	0	0	68.05	1773.86	1786.38	9.08	52.943
0	4	3	0	0	0	2	1	0	68.15	1774.00	1786.27	10.79	52.434
0	4	0	4	2	0	0	0	0	68.16	1773.78	1786.26	8.42	53.208
1	3	2	0	2	1	0	1	0	68.33	1774.07	1786.08	9.96	52.601
1	1	5	0	0	1	0	2	0	68.55	1774.13	1785.85	11.01	52.357
1	4	0	0	5	0	0	0	0	68.60	1773.45	1785.84	8.60	52.952
1	0	3	5	0	1	0	0	0	68.78	1773.13	1785.60	8.61	53.168
1	2	3	0	3	0	0	1	0	68.81	1773.51	1785.61	9.65	52.708
0	4	2	1	1	0	1	1	0	68.97	1773.60	1785.45	9.48	52.748
1	0	6	0	1	0	0	2	0	69.02	1773.57	1785.38	10.70	52.464
0	5	0	1	4	0	0	0	0	69.23	1772.98	1785.21	8.12	53.099
1	3	2	0	1	2	1	0	0	69.27	1772.97	1785.14	9.28	52.687
0	3	3	1	2	0	0	1	0	69.44	1773.04	1784.98	9.17	52.855
0	2	5	0	1	1	0	0	1	69.47	1774.30	1784.93	11.27	52.553
1	0	5	1	0	3	0	0	0	69.70	1770.97	1782.68	8.03	52.950
1	2	3	0	2	1	1	0	0	69.74	1772.41	1784.67	8.97	52.794
0	3	3	1	1	1	1	0	0	70.37	1771.94	1783.98	8.49	52.941
2	0	4	0	0	4	0	0	0	70.60	1772.00	1783.78	8.82	52.696
0	4	2	0	2	2	0	0	0	71.08	1771.62	1783.34	7.84	52.990
0	2	5	0	0	2	0	1	0	71.29	1771.68	1783.11	8.87	52.746
0	3	3	0	3	1	0	0	0	71.55	1771.06	1782.87	7.75	53.097
0	1	6	0	1	1	0	1	0	71.76	1771.12	1782.64	8.58	52.753
0	0	6	2	0	2	0	0	0	72.80	1769.94	1781.58	7.24	53.204

$V_M^{20°}$, ml./mol	λ°, cal/mole					log p, mm mercury				
	40—80 °C	70—110° C	90—130° C	110—150° C	130—170° C	60° C	90° C	110° C	130° C	150° C
209.849	2474.9	2377.7	2322.2	2272.8	2230.0	1.0024	1.6155	1.9508	2.2506	2.5141
211.311	2452.0	2370.5	2312.7	2260.2	2215.5	1.0485	1.6522	1.9850	2.2851	2.5505
213.341	2457.3	2367.3	2309.4	2257.8	2215.1	1.0629	1.6617	1.9977	2.2939	2.5577
196.535	—	—	—	—	—					
199.221	2490.7	2383.4	2334.3	2287.2	2244.3	0.9736	1.5210	1.8536	2.1554	2.4282
205.441	2532.9	2441.6	2381.5	2327.6	2270.7	0.9106	1.5410	1.8852	2.1972	2.4804
208.822	2573.2	2475.8	2413.4	2358.0	2303.2	0.8802	1.5190	1.8674	2.1840	2.4568
201.796	2478.8	2399.2	2343.9	2286.4	2241.5	0.9665	1.5483	1.8799	2.1883	2.4696
205.177	2519.1	2433.4	2375.8	2320.6	2274.0	0.9361	1.5263	1.8621	2.1751	2.4460
200.572	2507.0	2403.2	2350.1	2300.4	2255.6	0.9348	1.5221	1.8584	2.1626	2.4404
205.745	2547.3	2437.4	2382.0	2330.8	2288.1	0.9044	1.5001	1.8406	2.1494	2.4168
207.471	2538.2	2438.4	2378.2	2325.2	2270.3	0.9250	1.5515	1.8979	2.2060	2.4876
210.852	2578.5	2472.6	2410.1	2355.6	2302.8	0.8946	1.5295	1.8801	2.1928	2.4640
203.526	2484.1	2396.0	2340.6	2287.8	2241.1	0.9809	1.5588	1.8926	2.1971	2.4768
208.888	2563.6	2457.2	2397.8	2344.0	2299.4	0.8656	1.5012	1.8454	2.1566	2.4290
207.207	2524.4	2430.2	2372.5	2318.2	2273.6	0.9505	1.5368	1.8748	2.1839	2.4532
201.708	—	—	—	—	—					
194.528	—	—	—	—	—					
203.214	2476.2	2368.3	2319.2	2274.6	2233.6	0.9807	1.5672	1.8991	2.2001	2.4583
209.501	2543.5	2435.2	2374.9	2322.8	2269.9	0.9394	1.5620	1.9106	2.2148	2.4948
202.471	2449.1	2358.6	2305.4	2255.0	2208.2	1.0257	1.5913	1.9231	2.2191	2.5076
212.889	2583.8	2469.4	2406.8	2353.2	2302.4	0.9090	1.5400	1.8928	2.2016	2.4712
204.676	2453.3	2361.1	2309.7	2262.0	2219.1	1.0268	1.6039	1.9333	2.2346	2.4947
201.031	2399.2	2318.7	2272.1	2224.6	2189.9	1.0827	1.6112	1.9280	2.2257	2.4839
209.783	2484.5	2396.3	2337.8	2286.8	2233.8	1.0170	1.6333	1.9728	2.2780	2.5419
212.380	2546.0	2446.8	2384.1	2329.0	2284.5	0.9261	1.5484	1.8923	2.1999	2.4726
206.138	2430.4	2353.9	2300.2	2249.4	2204.6	1.0729	1.6406	1.9675	2.2691	2.5311
206.706	2458.6	2357.9	2306.4	2259.6	2218.7	1.0412	1.6144	1.9460	2.2434	2.5019
202.493	2376.3	2311.5	2262.6	2212.0	2175.4	1.1288	1.6479	1.9622	2.2602	2.5203
211.813	2489.8	2393.1	2334.5	2284.4	2233.4	1.0314	1.6438	1.9855	2.2868	2.5491
206.468	2434.6	2343.5	2290.3	2242.4	2197.5	1.0328	1.6375	1.9686	2.2638	2.5377
208.163	2435.7	2350.7	2296.9	2247.0	2204.2	1.0873	1.6511	1.9802	2.2779	2.5383
202.669	—	—	—	—	—					
210.308	2348.4	2275.6	2224.8	2177.4	2142.7	1.1563	1.7382	2.0557	2.3429	2.6006
207.930	2411.7	2336.3	2280.8	2229.8	2183.0	1.0789	1.6742	2.0028	2.2983	2.5741
209.960	2417.0	2333.1	2277.5	2227.4	2182.6	1.0933	1.6847	2.0155	2.3071	2.5813
206.816	2366.0	2286.0	2237.6	2192.4	2157.6	1.0958	1.6910	2.0088	2.2996	2.5570
210.810	2386.2	2298.2	2246.6	2201.6	2160.6	1.1392	1.7298	2.0562	2.3446	2.5992
207.165	2332.1	2255.8	2209.0	2164.2	2131.4	1.1951	1.7371	2.0509	2.3357	2.5884
212.272	2363.3	2291.0	2237.1	2189.0	2146.1	1.1853	1.7665	2.0901	2.3791	2.6356
202.148	2309.2	2248.6	2199.5	2151.6	2116.9	1.2412	1.7738	2.0851	2.3702	2.6248
213.800	2330.8	2265.2	2212.0	2162.4	2127.8	1.2168	1.7854	2.1026	2.3862	2.6442

TABLE 21

Values of molecular volumes V_M^{20} and densities d_4^{20}, experimental and calculated* according to the second method

Hydrocarbon	V_M^{20}, ml./mol		d_4^{20}, gm/mol		
	experimental from [51]	calculated from eq. (39)	experimental from [51]	experimental from eq. (56)	calculated from eq. (58)
n-Alkanes					
n-Pentane	115.20	114.58	0.6263	0.6297	0.62622
n-Hexane	130.95	130.69	0.65937	0.6594	0.65923
n-Heptane	146.56	146.80	0.68366	0.6825	0.68375
n-Octane	162.59	162.91	0.70252	0.7011	0.70267
n-Nonane	178.71	179.02	0.71763	0.7164	0.71771
n-Decane	194.93	195.12	0.72987	0.7292	0.72996
n-Undecane	210.96	211.23	0.74017	0.7400	0.74013
n-Dodecane	226.96	227.34	0.74869	0.7492	0.74870
2-Methylalkanes					
2-Methylbutane	116.43	116.21	0.61963	0.6208	0.61959
2-Methylpentane . . .	131.93	132.05	0.65315	0.6526	0.65326
2-Methylhexane	147.66	147.89	0.67859	0.6755	0.67843
2-Methylheptane . . .	163.66	163.72	0.69792	0.6977	0.69796
2-Methyloctane . . .	179.76	179.56	0.71346	0.7142	0.71355
2-Methylnonane . . .	195.88	195.40	0.72636	0.7281	0.72629
2-Methyldecane . . .	—	211.23	—	0.7399	0.73688
2-Methylundecane . .	—	227.08		0.7501	0.74584
3-Methylalkanes					
3-Methylpentane	129.72	129.73	0.66431	0.6642	0.66413
3-Methylhexane	145.82	145.80	0.68713	0.6872	0.68732
3-Methylheptane . . .	161.83	161.87	0.70582	0.7057	0.70577
3-Methyloctane . . .	177.95	177.93	0.72070	0.7208	0.72081
3-Methylnonane . . .	193.99	194.00	0.73340	0.7334	0.73330
3-Methyldecane . . .	—	210.07	—	0.7440	0.74384
3-Methylundecane . .	—	226.14	—	0.7532	0.75285
3-Ethylalkanes					
3-Ethylpentane	143.52	143.65	0.69816	0.6975	0.69816
3-Ethylhexane	160.07	159.92	0.71358	0.7143	0.71358
3-Ethylheptane	176.40	176.19	0.72700	0.7279	0.72600
3-Ethyloctane	192.26	192.46	0.74000	0.7392	0.73620
3-Ethylnonane	—	208.73	—	0.7488	0.74480
3-Ethyldecane	—	225.00	—	0.7570	0.75200
2,2-Dimethylalkanes					
2,2-Dimethylbutane . . .	132.74	132.73	0.64916	0.6492	0.6492
2,2-Dimethylpentane . .	148.69	148.62	0.67385	0.6742	0.6751
2,2-Dimethylhexane . . .	164.28	164.51	0.69528	0.6943	0.6953
2,2-Dimethylheptane . .	180.50	180.39	0.71050	0.7110	0.7114

*Equations for calculation:

$$(39)\ V_n^m = \alpha_v^m + \beta_v^m n; \quad (56)\ d_n^m = \frac{2.016 + 14.026\, n}{\alpha_v^m + \beta_v^m\, n}; \quad (58)\ d_n^m = A^m + \frac{B^m}{n_0^m + n}.$$

constants α_v^m, β_v^m, A^m, B^m, n_0^m being taken from Table 12.

TABLE 21 (contd.)

Hydrocarbon	V_M^{20}, ml./mol		d_4^{20}, gm/mol		
	experimental from [51]	calculated from eq. (39)	experimental from [51]	experimental from eq. (56)	calculated from eq. (58)
2,2-Dimethyloctane . . .	196.38	196.28	0.72450	0.7249	0.7245
2,2-Dimethylnonane . . .	—	212.17	—	0.7367	0.7354
2,2-Dimethyldecane . . .	—	228.06	—	0.7469	0.7447
2,3-Dimethylalkanes					
2,3-Dimethylpentane . .	144.15	144.17	0.69508	0.6950	0.6952
2,3-Dimethylhexane . .	160.40	160.39	0.71214	0.7122	0.7124
2,3-Dimethylheptane . .	176.65	176.61	0.72600	0.7262	0.7262
2,3-Dimethyloctane . . .	192.80	192.83	0.73793	0.7378	0.7375
2,3-Dimethylnonane . . .	—	209.05	—	0.7477	0.7469
2,3-Dimethyldecane . . .	—	225.27	—	0.7561	0.7548
2,4-Dimethylalkanes					
2,4-Dimethylhexane . .	163.09	162.94	0.70036	0.7010	0.70036
2,4-Dimethylheptane . .	179.12	179.32	0.71600	0.7152	0.71600
2,4-Dimethyloctane . . .	195.86	195.70	0.72640	0.7270	0.72640
2,4-Dimethylnonane . . .	—	212.08	—	0.7370	0.73380
2,4-Dimethyldecane . . .	—	228.46	—	0.7455	0.73940
3,3-Dimethylalkanes					
3,3-Dimethylpentane . .	144.53	144.70	0.69327	0.6925	0.6933
3,3-Dimethylhexane . . .	160.88	160.68	0.71000	0.7109	0.7101
3,3-Dimethylheptane . .	176.75	176.66	0.72560	0.7260	0.7253
3,3-Dimethyloctane . . .	192.52	192.64	0.73900	0.7386	0.7392
3,3-Dimethylnonane . . .	—	208.62	—	0.7492	0.7520
3,3-Dimethyldecane . . .	—	224.60	—	0.7584	0.7640
3,4-Dimethylalkanes					
3,4-Dimethylhexane . . .	158.81	159.01	0.71923	0.7183	0.7192
3,4-Dimethylheptane . .	175.35	174.96	0.73140	0.7330	0.7314
3,4-Dimethyloctane . . .	190.71	190.91	0.74600	0.7453	0.7460
3,4-Dimethylnonane . . .	—	206.86	—	0.7556	0.7630
3,4-Dimethyldecane . . .	—	228.81	—	0.7645	0.7860
2,(n-1)-Dimethylalkanes					
2,4-Dimethylpentane . .	148.95	148.86	0.67270	0.6731	0.6727
2,5-Dimethylhexane . . .	164.70	164.44	0.69354	0.6929	0.6935
2,6-Dimethylhexane . . .	180.91	180.82	0.70891	0.7090	0.7103
2,7-Dimethyloctane . . .	196.45	196.80	0.72420	0.7229	0.7242
2,8-Dimethylnonane . . .	—	212.78	—	0.7345	0.7360
2,9-Dimethyldecane . . .	—	228.76	—	0.7445	0.7460
2,2,(n-1)-Trimethylalkanes					
2,2,4-Trimethylpentane .	165.09	165.07	0.69188	0.6920	0.6919
2,2,5-Trimethylhexane . .	181.35	181.33	0.70721	0.7072	0.7072
2,2,6-Trimethylheptane .	197.60	197.59	0.71950	0.7200	0.7195
2,2,7-Trimethyloctane . .	—	213.85	—	0.7308	0.7300
2,2,8-Trimethylnonane . .	—	230.11	—	0.7401	0.7380
2,2,3,3-Tetramethylalkanes					
2,2,3,3-Tetramethylpentane	169.49	169.49	0.75666	0.7567	—
2,2,3,3-Tetramethylhexane	186.10	186.10	0.76450	0.7645	—
2,2,3,3-Tetramethylpentane	—	202.71	—	0.7711	—
2,2,3,3-Tetramethyloctane	—	219.32	—	0.7766	—

TABLE 22

Values of the constants α and β for the calculation[*]
of the heat of crystallization of n-alkanes in
different crystalline modifications

Hydrocarbon	L_A		L_B		L_C	
	α_A	β_A	α_B	β_B	α_C	β_C
n-Alkanes (n odd)	—	—	—	—	−2170	917
n-Alkanes (n even)	−2349	845	−3125	762	—	—

TABLE 23

Experimental and calculated[**] values of the heat
of crystallization of n-alkanes in different
crystalline modifications in cal/mol

n-Alkanes (n odd)	L_B		L_A		n-Alkanes (n even)	L_C	
	experimental from [49]	calculated from eq. (52)	experimental from [49]	calculated from eq. (51)		experimental from [49]	calculated from eq. (53)
n-Pentane	2011	1876	—	—	n-Butane	1608	1498
n-Heptane	3356	3566	—	—	n-Hexane	3126	3332
n-Nonane	5198	5256	3697	3733	n-Octane	4957	5166
n-Undecane	6940	6946	5301	5257	n-Decane	6863	7000
n-Tridecane	8643	8636	6812	6781	n-Dodecane	8804	8834
n-Pentadecane	10459	10326	8268	8305	n-Tetradecane	10772	10668
n-Heptadecane	—	12016	11400 (?)	9829	n-Hexadecane	12753	12502
n-Nonadecane	—	13706	—	11353	n-Octadecane	14450	14336
n-Heneicosane	—	15396	16900 (?)	12877	n-Eicosane	—	16170
n-Tricosane	24800 (?)	17086	19400 (?)	14401	n-Docosane	—	18004
n-Pentacosane	—	18776	18890 (?)	15925	n-Tetracosane	—	19838
n-Heptacosane	—	20466	—	17449	n-Hexacosane	—	21672
n-Nonacosane	—	22156	—	18973	n-Octacosane	—	23506
					n-Triacontane	—	25340

[*]According to equations (51) to (53) of the second method.
[**]Equations for calculation:

$$(51)\ L_A = \alpha_A + \beta_A\, n; \quad (52)\ L_B = \alpha_B + \beta_B\, n; \quad (53)\ L_C = \alpha_C + \beta_C\, n.$$

Constants $\alpha_A,\ \alpha_B,\ \alpha_C,\ \beta_A,\ \beta_B,\ \beta_C$ are taken from Table 22.

TABLE 24

Experimental and calculated* boiling points of n-alkanes and alkanes of other homologous groups (at a pressure of 760 mm mercury)

Hydrocarbon	t_{boil}, °C		
	experimental from [10]	calculated from eq. (67)	calculated from [10]
n-Alkanes			
n-Pentane	36.073	36.02	36.077
n-Hexane	68.740	68.49	68.749
n-Heptane	98.428	98.25	98.445
n-Octane	125.665	125.63	125.663
n-Nonane	150.798	150.90	150.784
n-Decane	174.123	174.29	174.108
n-Undecane	195.893	196.02	195.875
n-Dodecane	216.278	216.24	216.280
n-Tridecane	—	235.12	235.483
n-Tetradecane	—	252.78	253.618
n-Pentadecane	—	269.33	270.798
n-Hexadecane	—	284.88	287.118
n-Heptadecane	—	299.52	302.660
n-Octadecane	—	313.31	317.495
n-Nonedecane	—	326.35	331.685
n-Eicosane	—	338.67	345.283
2-Methylalkanes			
2-Methylbutane	27.852	27.81	—
2-Methylpentane	60.272	60.20	—
2-Methylhexane	90.052	90.05	—
2-Methylheptane	117.646	117.66	—
2-Methyloctane	143.263	143.26	—
2-Methylnonane	167.000	167.06	—
2-Methyldecane	—	189.26	189.20
2-Methylundecane	—	210.00	210.00
2-Methyldodecane	—	229.48	229.50
2-Methyltridecane	—	247.70	247.)

*Equation for calculation (67):

$$t_{boil} = t_0^m + \frac{C^m}{n_0^{m+n}}.$$

n-Alkanes, $t_{boil} = 782.179 - \dfrac{16\,401.98}{17.982 + n}$; 2-Methylalkanes, $t_{boil} = 822.93 -$

$- \dfrac{18724.45}{18,549 + n}$; 3-Methylalkanes, $t_{boil} = 934.97 - \dfrac{25591.11}{23.358 + n}$; 3-Ethylalkanes,

$t_{boil} = 2683.02 - \dfrac{265104.15}{95.375 + n}$; 2,2-Dimethylalkanes, $t_{boil} = 983.95 - \dfrac{28700.80}{24.722 + n}$;

2,3-Dimethylalkanes, $t_{boil} = 1246.52 - \dfrac{50390.25}{36.562 + n}$; 2,(n-1)-Dimethylalkanes, t_{boil}

$= 818.62 - \dfrac{18379.66}{17.90 + n}$; 3,3-Dimethylalkanes, $t_{boil} = 1603.43 - \dfrac{87344.37}{50.563 + n}$.

<u>TABLE 24</u> (contd.)

Hydrocarbon	t_{boil}, °C		
	experimental from [10]	calculated from eq. (67)	calculated from [10]
2-Methyltetradecane	—	264.80	265.40
2-Methylpentadecane	—	281.00	281.90
2-Methylhexadecane	—	296.00	297.70
2-Methylheptadecane	—	311.00	313.00
2-Methyloctadecane	—	324.00	327.00
2-Methylnonadecane	—	337.00	341.00
3-Methylalkanes			
3-Methylpentane	63.282	63.28	—
3-Methylhexane	91.851	92.00	—
3-Methylheptane	118.925	118.88	—
3-Methyloctane	144.180	144.10	—
3-Methylnonane	167.800	167.80	—
3-Methyldecane	—	190.10	—
3-Methylundecane	—	211.20	—
3-Methyldodecane	—	231.10	—
3-Methyltridecane	—	249.90	—
3-Methyltetradecane	—	267.80	—
3-Methylpentadecane	—	284.80	—
3-Methylhexadecane	—	301.00	—
3-Methylheptadecane	—	316.00	—
3-Methyloctadecane	—	331.00	—
3-Methylnonedecane	—	345.00	—
3-Ethylalkanes			
3-Ethylpentane	93.475	93.49	—
3-Ethylhexane	118.534	118.54	—
3-Ethylheptane	143.100	143.10	—
3-Ethyloctane	—	167.20	—
3-Ethylnonane	—	190.90	—
3-Ethyldecane	—	214.10	—
3-Ethylundecane	—	236.90	—
3-Ethyldedecane	—	259.20	—
3-Ethyltridecane	—	281.20	—
3-Ethyltetradecane	—	303.00	—
2,2-Dimethylalkanes			
2,2-Dimethylbutane	49.741	49.74	—
2,2-Dimethylpentane	79.198	79.19	—
2,2-Dimethylhexane	106.840	106.84	—
2,2-Dimethylheptane	—	132.80	—
2,2-Dimethyloctane	—	157.40	—

TABLE 24 (contd.)

Hydrocarbon	t boil, °C		
	experimental from [10]	calculated from eq. (67)	calculated from [10]
2,2-Dimethylnonane	—	180.50	—
2,2-Dimethyldecane	—	202.40	—
2,2-Dimethylundecane	—	223.10	—
2,2-Dimethyldodecane	—	242.80	—
2,2-Dimethyltridecane	—	261.00	—
2,2-Dimethyltetradecane	—	279.00	—
2,3-Dimethylalkanes			
2,3-Dimethylpentane	89.784	89.78	—
2,3-Dimethylhexane	115.607	115.74	—
2,3-Dimethylheptane	140.650	140.55	—
2,3-Dimethyloctane	164.310	164.31	—
2,3-Dimethylnonane	—	187.10	—
2,3-Dimethyldecane	—	208.90	—
2,3-Dimethylundecane	—	229.80	—
2,3-Dimethyldodecane	—	249.90	—
2,3-Dimethyltridecane	—	269.30	—
2,3-Dimethyltetradecane	—	288.00	—
2,(n-1)-Dimethylalkanes			
2,4-Dimethylpentane	80.500	80.49	—
2,5-Dimethylhexane	109.103	108.99	—
2,6-Dimethylheptane	135.210	135.37	—
2,7-Dimethyloctane	159.870	159.86	—
2,8-Dimethylnonane	—	182.70	—
2,9-Dimethyldecane	—	203.90	—
2,10-Dimethylundecane	—	223.80	—
2,11-Dimethyldodecane	—	242.50	—
2,12-Dimethyltridecane	—	260.00	—
2,13-Dimethyltetradecane	—	275.50	—
3,3-Dimethylalkanes			
3,3-Dimethylpentane	86.064	86.06	—
3,3-Dimethylhexane	111.969	111.98	—
3,3-Dimethylheptane	137.012	137.02	—
3,3-Dimethyloctane	—	161.20	—
3,3-Dimethylnonane	—	184.60	—
3,3-Dimethyldecane	—	207.30	—
3,3-Dimethylundecane	—	229.30	—
3,3-Dimethyldodecane	—	250.60	—
3,3-Dimethyltridecane	—	271.20	—
3,3-Dimethyltetradecane	—	291.00	—

TABLE 25

Values of constants A and B in the equation
$P = A \log p + B$. The equation connects a
certain property P (V_M^{20} of liquid alkanes,
$\Delta H°$ (el.,gas) at 25°C, $L°_{vap}$ of alkanes
in an ideal gaseous state at 50°C) with
the logarithm of the vapour pressure $\bar{p}$
of liquid alkanes at 60°C. The
vapour pressure P refers to mm
mercury

Homologous group of alkanes	V_M^{20}, ml./mol		$\Delta H°$ (el.,gas) at 25°C. kcal/mol		$L°_{vap}$ (150°C) cal/mol	
	A	B	A	B	A	B
n-Alkanes	234.89	—37.91	—71.46	11.40	12412	—2005
2-Methylalkanes	241.63	—38.24	—74.58	11.40	12248	—1927
3-Methylalkanes	240.24	—38.97	—74.82	11.92	12141	—1903
2,2-Dimethylalkanes . .	250.22	—38.90	—79.67	11.69	12088	—1933
2,(n-1)-Dimethylalkanes .	245.28	—37.15	—78.33	11.58	12659	—2172
2,2,(n-1)-Trimethylalkanes	253.55	—37.12	—	—	12076	—1918
3-Ethylalkanes	247.35	—43.21	—77.08	—13.21	—	—
3,3-Dimethylalkanes . .	252.11	—42.69	—77.38	11.59	12366	—2070

REFERENCES

[1] F.D. ROSSINI, Research Nat. Bur. Standards, 13, No.1, 21 (1934).

[2] F.D. ROSSINI, Chem. Rev., 27, No.1, 1 (1940).

[3] R.S. JESSUP, Research Nat. Bur. Standards, 18, No.2, 115 (1937).

[4] R.H. EWELL, Ind. Eng. Chem., 32, No.6, 778 (1940).

[5] W.I. TAYLOR, I.M. PIGNOCCO, F.D. ROSSINI, Research Nat. Bur. Standards, 34, No.5, 413 (1945).

[6] E.I. PROSEN, W.H. JOHNSON, F.D. ROSSINI, Research Nat. Bur. Standards, 37, 51 (1946).

[7] H. WINER, J.Chem. Phys., 15, 766 (1947); Phys. Chem., 52, 1082 (1948).

[8] D.R. PLATT, J. Phys. Chem., 56, 328 (1952).

[9] J.B. GREENSHIELDS, F.D. ROSSINI, J. Phys. Chem., 62, No.3, 27 (1958).

[10] M.D. TILICHEYEV and A.V. IOGANSEN, Zh. fiz. khim, 24, No.7, 770 (1950).

[11] M.D. TILICHEYEV and A.V. IOGANSEN, Zh. fiz. khim, 25, No.11, 1295 (1951).

[12] M.D. TILICHEYEV and V.M. TATEVSKII, Neft. khoz., 26, No. 12, 33 (1948).

[13] V.A. KIREYEV, Zh. fiz. khim, 2, 233 (1931).

[14] V.A. KIREYEV, Zh. priklad. khim., 7, No.1, 1 (1934).

[15] M. Kh. KARAPET'YANTS, Zh. fiz. khim., XXIX, No.6, 1132; No.7, 1328 (1955).

[16] M. Kh. KARAPET'YANTS, Zh. fiz. khim., XXX, No.10, 2218 (1956).

[17] H.I. BERNSTEIN, J. Chem. Phys., 20, No.2, 263 (1952).

[18] K.I. LAIDER, Canad. J. Chem., 34, No.5, 623 (1956).

[19] V.M. Tatevskii, Dokl. Akad. Nauk. SSSR., LXXIV, No.2, 287 (1950).

[20] V.M. TATEVSKII, Vest. Mosk. gos. univ., 10, 53 (1950).

[21] V.M. TATEVSKII, V.V. KOROBOV, E.A. MENDOZHERITSKII, Dokl. Akad. Nauk, SSSR, LXXIV, No.4, 743 (1950).

[22] V.M. TATEVSKII, E.A. MENDZHERITSKII, V.V. KOROBOV, Vest. Mosk. gos. univ., 5, 83 (1951).

[23] V.M. TATEVSKII, Dokl. Akad. Nauk. SSSR., LXXV, No.6, 819 (1950).

[24] V.M. TATEVSKII, Vest. Mosk. gos. univ., 6, 53 (1951).

[25] V.M. TATEVSKII, Zh. fiz. khim., XXV, No.2, 241 (1951).

[26] V.M. TATEVSKII, Diss., Mosc. Stat. Univ., (1951).

[27] V.M. TATEVSKII and Yu. A. PENTIN, Vest. Mosk. gos. univ., 5, 69 (1953).

[28] V.M. TATEVSKII, V.V. KOROBOV, E.A. MENDZHERITSKII, Dokl. Akad. Nauk. SSSR., LXXVIII, No.1, 67 (1951).

[29] V.M. TATEVSKII, Yu. A. Pentin, Vest. Mosk. gos. univ., 3, 81 (1954).

[30] V.M. TATEVSKII, Dokl. Akad. Nauk. SSSR., 109, No.1, 131 (1956).

[31] V.M. TATEVSKII, Chemical structure of hydrocarbons and rules obeyed by their physico-chemical properties (Khimicheskoye stroyenie uglevodorodov i zakonomernosti v ikh fiziko-khimicheskikh svoistvakh), Mosc. Stat. Univ. (1953).

[32] V.M. TATEVSKII, Uch. zap. Mosk. gos. univ., 174, 235 (1955).

[33] V.M. TATEVSKII, <u>Dokl. Akad. Nauk. SSSR</u>, 101, No.3, 515 (1955).

[34] V.M. TATEVSKII, <u>Dokl. Akad. Nauk. SSSR</u>, 101, No.5, 901 (1955).

[35] V.M. TATEVSKII, Yu. A. PENTIN, <u>Vest. Mosk. gos. univ.</u>, 2, 21 (1955).

[36] V.M. TATEVSKII, <u>Dokl. Akad. Nauk. SSSR</u>, 113, No.4, 836 (1957).

[37] V.I. ZIBOROV, Yu. A. PENTIN, V.M. TATEVSKII, <u>Zh. fiz. khim.</u>, XXXII, No.3, 707 (1958).

[38] V.M. TATEVSKII, V.A. BENDERSKII, <u>Zh. obshch. khim.</u>, XXVIII, 1733 (1958).

[39] V.M. TATEVSKII, Yu. A. PENTIN, V.A. ZIBOROV, V.A. BENDERSKII, N. NIKITIN and A.A. BOLDIN, <u>Uch. zap. Kazan Univ.</u>

[40] V.M. TATEVSKII, <u>Zh. obshch. khim.</u>, XXVIII, No.11, 2935 (1958).

[41] V.M. TATEVSKII, <u>Zh. fiz. khim.</u>, XXXII, No.6, 1226 (1958).

[42] V.M. TATEVSKII, <u>Zh. fiz. khim.</u>, XXXII, No.5, 1168 (1958).

[43] V.M. TATEVSKII and S.S. YAROVOI, <u>Zh. obshch. khim.</u>, In press.

[44] V.M. TATEVSKII, <u>Vest. Mosk. gos. univ.</u>, 4, 205 (1958).

[45] V.M. TATEVSKII, Yu. G. PAPULOV, <u>Dokl. Akad. Nauk. SSSR</u>, 126, No.4, 823 (1959).

[46] V.M. TATEVSKII, Yu. G. PAPULOV, <u>Zh. fiz. khim.</u> In press.

[47] Kh. S. BAGDASARYAN, <u>Zh. fiz. khim.</u>, XXIV, No.11, 1326 (1950).

[48] Yu. A. ZHDANOV, Homology in organic chemistry (Gomologiya v organicheskoi khimii), <u>Mosc. Stat. Univ.</u> (1950).

[49] M.D. TILICHEYEV, Physico-chemical properties of indivi-
     dual hydrocarbons (Fiziko-khimicheskiye svoistva
     individual'nikh uglevodorodov) No. V, ch. XV,
     Gostoptekhizdat (1954).

[50] F.D. ROSSINI et al. Selected values of properties of
     Hydrocarbons, Washington (1953).

[51] M.D. TILICHEYEV, Physico-chemical properties of indivi-
     dual hydrocarbons (Fiziko-khimicheskiye svoistva
     individual'nikh uglevodorodov), No. III, ch. IX;
     No. IV ch. XIII; No. V, supplements to ch. IV, IX,
     XIII, Gostoptekhizdat (1951-1954).

[52] A.K. SUSHKEVICH, Theory of numbers (Teoriya chisel),
     Kharkov University (1954).

[53] T. SKOLEM, Diophantische Gleichungen, Berlin (1938).

[54] S. MIDZUSIMA, Structure of molecules and internal
     rotation (Stroyeniye molekul i unutrenneye vrash-
     cheniye). For. Lang. Pub. Hs. (1957).